I Have Lived Before

The True story of the reincarnation of Shanti Devi

By Sture Lönnerstrand

Translated by Leslie Kippen

P.O. Box 754 • Huntsville, AR 72740-0754

Originally titled: *Shanti Devi, en berättelse om reinkarnation.*
First published 1994 by **Larsons Förlag, Sweden.**

Library of Congress Cataloging-in-Publication Data
Lönnerstrand, Sture, 1919–
I Have Lived Before, by Sture Lönnerstrand
Translated from the Swedish by Leslie Kippen
Biography and interviews dealing with the story of Shanti Devi.
Fully verified case of reincarnation in India.
1. Reincarnation. 2. Life after Death. 3. Spirituality.
4. India.
I. Lönnerstrand, Sture, 1919– II. Shanti Devi, 1926– III. Title
Library of Congress Catalog Card Number: 98-65383
ISBN 1-886940-03-7

Cover Design: Lawrence Levy, Drawing Board Studios
Book set in: Jansen and University Roman
Book Design: Kris Kleeberg
Photos: Tom Cannon

Check Our Web Site!
www.ozarkmt.com

P.O. Box 754
Huntsville, AR 72740-0754
Printed in the United States of America

Table of Contents

Section 2

List of Photographs

FRONTISPIECE: Shanti Devi Mathur

AUTHOR: Sture Lönnerstrand

This is a picture of the Indian girl, Shanti Devi Mathur. She remembers her previous life in minute detail. Shanti Devi even has distinct recollections from the time in between both incarnations.

In her previous life her name was Lugdi Devi Chanbey. Lugdi Devi was born on January 18, 1902 in the town of Mathura (Muttra) located approximately fifteen miles south of Delhi.

On September 25, 1925 her son Naunita Lal was born. Several days later, on October 4th, Lugdi Devi died at Lady Lyall's hospital in Agra due to complications after the birth.

After one year, two months and seven days, on December 11, 1926 she reincarnated in Delhi and was given the name Shanti Devi.

Lugdi Devi / Shanti Devi is the best documented case of reincarnation that the modern reincarnation research is familiar with.

Introduction

All through the ages people have asked themselves if there is life after death.

At the present time as well as in earlier times, the teachings about reincarnation are a living reality for billions of people over the whole world and is a foundation of two of the world's great religions, Hinduism and Buddhism.

The teachings about reincarnation were also for several hundred years a part of the Christian religion, but it was finally forbidden in the 6th century during a church meeting in Constantinople. Today, there are very few people who know this fact.

The formulation is as follows, which the members of the church agreed upon and which forbade the earlier Christian belief in rebirth or reincarnation:

> "Each and everyone who supports the mystical idea of the soul's earlier existence and consequent series of events (karma or the law of cause-and-effect) shall be damned (anathema)."

According to the teachings of reincarnation, life continues in constantly-changing new forms until the final goal, which is an everlasting union with the Godhead, has been attained.

Shanti Devi, which the main part of this book is about (part 2 discusses karma and reincarnation in more general terms), remembers her latest former life in minute detail.

In her previous incarnation she was born in the town of Mathura in northern India and was given the name Lugdi Devi. She lived a happy life but died when she was only 23 years old in complications resulting from child-birth. A little over one year later she reincarnated in Delhi as Shanti Devi.

This is the best documented case of reincarnation that modern reincarnation research is familiar with. It is also the most discussed.

Mahatma Gandhi, India's beloved leader, took a great interest in Shanti Devi and made it possible for an impartial Committee of Inquiry to verify her statements.

I myself, have on several occasions during long conversations with Shanti Devi been able to experience her unusual story. Moreover I have spoken to her nearest family members and other relatives from her two lives and with members of the Committee as well as with others who have a good insight into this remarkable story.

Sture Lönnerstrand

1

"You Are not my real Mama"

"Mama, where is the picture of Krishna?"

The little girl is sitting looking out through the open doors towards the flat roof which serves as a courtyard.

The noise from Moonshine Street, Chandni Chauk, increases its pitch in the pale morning mist. The girl hears the cries from the vendors down below. She is listening intensely. From the roof between lines of laundry, where brightly colored pieces of material are hanging like flags, she can see the ancient town with its conglomeration of houses painted in white and green.

"Mama, where is the picture of Krishna?"

For Shanti Devi it's as if there are two worlds each on either side of a transparent membrane, one which is real and one which is shadowy.

Here she sits, tiny and delicate and wrapped in a large shawl so that she won't catch cold before the heat of the day sets in.

Somewhere out there is the other *Real* woman. At first, she didn't know exactly what the Real woman did, but now she knows. She sees that she is sitting by her well and polishing her silver vessels before her husband is about to come home. Earlier she had often tried to find that well when she went out into the courtyard, but it wasn't there.

The *Real* woman is slim and beautiful. She is wearing a sari which glitters in red and gold. She is as fragile as a doll and has a sad, yet at the same time a happy face.

Her eyes are large—too large. She has finely depicted eyebrows, a full mouth, and in the middle of her forehead the bindu (holy) mark, which signifies that she is married, and of course, lots of expensive jewelry. On her forehead she has a pearl trinket which is fastened over her hair. She is wearing earrings and has a pearl in one of her nostrils. She is also wearing a wide necklace, a bracelet and rings. Her ankle-bracelets jingle as she moves.

"What do you want, Shanti Devi? Mother is at the bazaar."

Her sister's voice pierces through all the other noises. The voice is unfamiliar. Shanti Devi's eyes fill with tears. Her older sister comes up to her sulkily. "What are you crying about? Nobody has hurt you."

"I'm not crying."

Everything is so indifferent and meaningless. This world is not the Real world, but it exists nevertheless. She can't explain it.

In the beginning, everything mingled together in an impenetrable confusion and it was extremely painful. Now she can see with distinct clarity.

A brahminwife from Muttra

"Why don't you speak properly, and answer when people speak to you."

"It was the picture of Krishna," says Shanti Devi. "I thought I had it."

"You think too much."

Her sister is tired of little Shanti Devi's chatter and fancied wild dreams. It started just after her 4th birthday. Earlier she had been silent and uncommunicative, far too quiet. They had almost been afraid that she was ill. She didn't babble as most small children do.

Lately she had begun to express herself clearly, but yet in some way unnaturally.

"Yes, we had a picture of Krishna which I love. When I had been sitting in the courtyard and had finished polishing the silver vessels I would go into my prayer-room and pray. I was anxious, but my husband ..."

"Your husband, what stupid talk is that?"

Shanti Devi starts to cry once again and her sister regrets what she has said. She sits beside the little girl and tries to caress and console her.

"Tell me everything. So you have a husband? You are married?"

"Leave me alone. What do you mean? Who are you?"

"Dear Shanti Devi, you know quite well that I am your older sister. Are you not awake yet?"

"I am awake. You were angry with me, and I didn't recognize you. The others are always friendly towards me."

"You were married then. Let's play that we are married."

"It's not a game."

"Why do you say that? What does that mean?"

Shanti Devi straightens herself up and a somewhat grown-up and dignified expression appears on her little face. She moves away from her sister and regards her defiantly. She is proud.

"I am a brahminwife from Muttra. I'm not living with you. This is not my Real home. You are not my Real sister. These clothes that I am wearing are not my Real clothes. You have nothing to do with me."

"Dear Shanti Devi, you mustn't say that. You don't have any other home. You don't have any other clothes."

"My home is in Muttra."

"What is Muttra? There can't be something called Muttra."

"I am married there."

"You are too small to be married."

"I'm not small, I'm grown-up. I'm waiting ..."

"What are you waiting for?"

"I'm awaiting the birth of a baby. That's why I'm praying to Krishna who you've taken away from me."

Her sister crouches forward and roars with laughter.

"I have never heard anything so ridiculous! Now you have really surpassed yourself with your stupidity. Mama must know about this."

I want my red sari

Shanti Devi sits still and looks at her sister. She feels mocked and insulted. It's true, she is small, she is only a child. But she knows much more than a child because she feels a Real woman's feelings. Now she doesn't want to speak about it anymore—it's pointless. The others would not understand.

Steps are heard on the stairs. Prem Pyari, the children's mother has come home with a heavy load of parcels. She is strong and robust, but her face is fragile and sensitive.

"Oh, it's hot today. The summer is on its way. Oh, I'm so warm."

The older of the two girls runs towards her and throws her arms around her neck.

"Mama, mama, Shanti Devi is so strange again. She has asked for the picture of Krishna again. She says that this is not her real home and that she is pregnant. She is crazy!"

"Quiet, quiet, calm down," says Prem Pyari reassuringly. "Pretend that nothing has happened. There must be something wrong with her, poor thing. Go to school now, but promise me one thing."

"Yes, mama."

"Don't laugh at Shanti Devi. She is your sister after all. She just can't help it. Some children are like that. I hope you understand. It's just that in her case, it's stronger and more pronounced."

The mother goes into the room where Shanti Devi is sitting and bends over and kisses her.

"How is Mama's little girl? Mama is going to give you something beautiful if you're a really good girl."

"You are not my Real mama," says Shanti Devi resolutely. "You don't look like her."

"Now she's telling me I'm not her real mother. That was a surprise. Can you guess what's in this parcel?"

"I don't care what's in it. I want my picture of Krishna back. This is not my Real home."

"Don't you understand, it makes mama so upset when you say that. Now let's open the parcel so that you can see what's in it. I've bought a length of good-quality material at the bazaar for you and your sister. Look, it's silk. Now perhaps you can have your first real sari."

She holds up the material and Shanti Devi touches it briefly.

"I usually do wear a sari, but this is of poor quality. I don't want it."

"Has one heard such a child? A four-year old expressing her opinion about the quality of a piece of material. It's silk from Banares."

"They have deceived you. Some merchants are so unreliable."

"What sort of child is this? What do you know about material, you who are so small?"

"I'm not small at all. My husband knows much more than I do. He buys and sells material and many other goods. If you give me my own sari, you'll see that it is of much better quality."

Her sister giggles by the doorway. Her mother gives her a stern glance.

"I want my red sari and my jewelry. Let me have my chand, my rings, my bracelets and my chureys. You have taken my chureys."

"Chureys, what do you mean? I should do the right thing and tell your father."

I've done it all before

Shanti Devi looks up at her mother's face. Her familiar features are partly as they should be, but yet so different and unfamiliar.

It's the same with everything else as well. The Real world, why does it have to disappear as if it had only been there in her thoughts. She has lost everything that belongs to her.

Shanti Devi covers her face with her hands. Her little body is shaking with sobs.

"I want to go home. Please let me go back to my home."

"But little Shanti Devi," says her mother affectionately, "you are home. Where do you want to go?"

"I want to travel to Muttra. I live there."

"My dear child, this must be something you have dreamed. Perhaps there is a town called Muttra, but how could you possibly know? Am I not your mother? Is this not your home."

"Not my Real home. That's only in Muttra."

"But this is your home anyway."

"Yes," sulks Shanti Devi in a resigned manner, "this is my home, I suppose. You are my mama in any case."

"I'm glad to hear it. You may go out onto the roof and play now. Afterwards perhaps mama will come and tell you the story about Rama, the hero who conquered India's enemies and about Sita whom he loved."

"Perhaps someone else will be coming as well," whispers Shanti Devi.

"You're speaking so faintly, I can't hear what you're saying."

"Someone else might be coming too, my Jeth, but I won't say anymore."

"Who is that? What do you mean?"

"I can't tell you. You won't believe me anyway. I've done it all before."

"Little Shanti Devi, you've done it all before. I understand. If I tell you we will take you to Muttra some time later on when you are a bit older, will you please promise me you will be good and obedient and not talk about all this unnecessarily, so mama won't be upset. Can you promise me that?"

"Yes, I shall try. That's if you promise me something else. I would like you to give me a picture of Krishna, so that I can pray. I would like a picture like the one I had before ..."

"Before?"

"Before that which is so hard to understand happened. No, I can't talk about it. I don't really know. It was before ... I was so afraid and I asked for help. Then everything became dark."

My doll, my beloved doll

The little girl is sitting on a bench on the roof. Behind the doors her mother is busy with her housework. It's warm.

Now and then Prem Pyari peers out somewhat worriedly, but Shanti Devi plays calmly with her dolls and card games—round cards with colorful and gracious, sometimes grotesque pictures.

Shanti Devi is quiet and subdued. On the outside she's no different from other small children. But within, she feels a longing which can't be described. It's a strong feeling and difficult to understand. Somewhere outside this limited corner of the world which she can't leave, there is a Real world, a Real life.

She hears the distinct voice of a man clearly above the murmur from the street. "Doll, where is my beloved doll? Come—my beloved doll! This is our house, our new house. Do you like it?"

It's not the first time. She has heard it many times before. She recognizes it so well.

The voice always returns and the Real woman in the red sari with the intricately woven gold-threads speaks to her husband. Shanti herself doesn't know what it means to remember. Everything becomes so alive and intensive, sometimes so incredibly painful. At first she didn't realize it was herself who was the Real woman.

"Dear doll! Lugdi Devi! I shall show you the house. Let's go in. You are as shy as a small child. This is your new home," the man's voice says.

"Why was I given such a name by my parents? I am no doll, not a child. I am grown-up, I am your wife."

Lugdi Devi means "heavenly doll." That is the Real woman's name, the one she was known by. Now she hears her husband's name as well.

She sees the large, beautiful house which is their home. It's a brilliant yellow in the sunshine. It's an elegant house which one would expect of a Chaubey on the Chaubey street in Muttra.

Amidst the sunny day in a kaleidoscopic throng of images and noises, the well-known town with its thousand spires can be seen. It is Krishna's town.

Here the street is blue. Between all these houses which she has seen so often, she can now be seen travelling to Jumna, the holy river, to the pool by the temple and baths.

There is the clocktower with the great gates. She can see it from afar. She's travelling under it in a tonga, a small horse-carriage.

She's really happy. She's pregnant, and now she has been to the large Dvarkadish temple and made a sacrifice of flowers, fruit and pastries.

"Please be gracious towards your humble servant, Lugdi Devi! Allow me to give birth to a son, Dvarkadish!"

She'll get better

Rang Bahadur Mathur, Shanti Devi's father, has just come home from his office. He is tired after a hard day's work. He has a small agency with a couple of employees, and he works hard to be able to make a modest living at it.

"How is Shanti Devi?" he asks.

Prem Pyari had at first not wanted to worry her husband, but when he asked she must tell him.

"When she becomes excited her voice changes," says Prem Pyari. "She speaks as if she had come from another place."

Rand Bahadur reflects:

"Muttra," he says, "it's Mathura. The people in Mathura always say Muttra when talking about their town. How can our girl know that? Here in this house there is nobody who has spoken to her about Mathura or Muttra."

"She doesn't meet anyone but us," says Prem Pyari. "She hasn't even been down on the street. She asked for a picture of Krishna. Mathura is Krishna's birthplace."

"The girl hasn't uttered a word until quite recently. We have worried in case she was dumb, but then she began to speak properly several weeks ago. Long sentences. But she spoke a strange dialect. Who could have taught her?"

"A child can fantasize and make up a little of everything," says Prem Pyari understandingly, "but it must come from somewhere. What she says must have an explanation."

"Shanti Devi cannot have any idea about how children come into this world. Have we spoken about such things in her presence? Where does she get the idea that she is pregnant?"

"She'll probably get better if we leave her alone."

Forbidden food

Now the servant comes in who is also the cook and says that the evening meal is served.

The mother fetches little Shanti Devi who is outside on the roof and her older sister comes in as well. The family sits themselves down on the cushions on the floor to eat. The father gives Shanti Devi a kiss. She bends her head with the small dark plaits and places it against his knee.

"She is sweet and well behaved," mumbles Rang Bahadur. "Why do people always say there is something wrong with her? She can be a great writer when she grows up."

Everyone laughs except Shanti Devi who doesn't move a muscle. The family helps themselves to the tender chicken. The bowls are filled with rice, but when it's Shanti's turn she defiantly puts up both hands.

"No, I don't want food like this," she says.

"You don't like chicken?" says her father good-naturedly. "It's absolutely fresh and tastes excellent. It melts in the mouth. Please *do* have a bit of chicken and some rice."

"I can eat the rice, but I want satvic food."

"What is she saying?" exclaims her mother embarrassed. "Aren't you ashamed of yourself, child?"

"She wants satvic food," repeats her father. "Satvic. Where have you learned that word?"

"It's a word which we use in Muttra. We don't eat meat. It's not right to kill animals and a terrible crime to eat them. People eat meat anyway, but we don't do it," says the girl.

"Who are *we*?"

"In Muttra we don't eat meat. I personally make quite

sure that my husband is served satvic food and the servants are not allowed to touch what he eats. When he comes home from his store by the Dvarkadish temple everything is ready to be served. I taste the food first and serve him myself. He likes it that way."

Prem Pyari's face is as red as a beetroot. Rang Bahadur sits quietly and thoughtful. Her sister stares horrified towards Shanti Devi. That which has just taken place is a serious insult towards the master of the house. Shanti Devi seems to have lost all respect for her parents.

"We eat our food in our way, you eat yours, your way. We have our clothes, you have yours. I want my clothes and my chureys."

"Leave the table," says Prem Pyari. "You'll have to go to bed hungry. I don't want to see you here."

"No, no," says Rang Bahadur violently. "Leave her alone. She doesn't know what she's saying and yet it is in some way correct. You need not be here and eat with us if you don't want to. Would you like some fruit?

"Thank you," says Shanti Devi. "I can prepare my food by myself."

"We will allow you to prepare your own food. Go now my girl, nobody is annoyed with you."

She's living another life

"Chureys," mumbles Rang Bahadur. "Where have I heard that expression before? Chand, that is a trinket or a piece of jewelry worn on the forehead, but the word chureys is not correct Hindi. God, what shall we do with this child? We can't forbid her to speak!"

"I wonder why our karma is so bad that we have been given a mentally disordered daughter," says Prem Pyari sadly. "We must do as she asks and provide her with an altarpiece with Krishna's picture. When I lived with my parents we prayed every day. Prayers always help."

"Mentally disordered, prayers, karma," says Rang Bahadur impatiently. "She is far too wise, that girl. We ought to ask a doctor for advice, but I wonder if even a doctor would believe us."

"She's living another life," says the mother.

The servant comes in and clears the table.

"Another life," repeats Rang Bahadur. "Do you know what you're saying, Prem Pyari? You have spoken openly about something which I have in secret been afraid of for a long time. No, Shanti Devi must not speak without thinking any longer. She must be silenced. She could be in great danger."

"I don't understand," says Prem Pyari anxiously. "Have we done something wrong?"

"How does one know what is right or wrong? If it is true that the girl remembers her previous life then she is doomed to unhappiness, as that is what is written in the ancient scriptures. No person knows about such things. This is the greatest misfortune which could have happened to us. We'll be punished, and how can we protect our daughter? What have we done, my dear wife? What *have* we done?"

Who Am I?

In that part of the Indian capital where Shanti Devi lives, it's extremely overcrowded. Door against door, stairs pressed in on all sides.

Where the streets are narrowest it's always dark, but here and there daylight manages to filter through with a fine ray of sunshine sharp and white as a javelin.

There is a small temple further away.

A song is heard between the walls of the houses. Light is followed by the faint, resounding sound from the beat of a drum.

The light finds it way into the wider streets where the bazaar is located. Sweet and pungent odors penetrate the air. The sound of wagons squeaking is mixed with the vendor's shouts and in the distance can be heard the horn of a motorcar.

A little girl in a beautiful yellow sari comes walking along. She slows down when she hears the song and she remains stationary beside a stairway.

Not far away from the bazaar is a large and well-kept house. A servant is sweeping the pathway in front of the house.

Two small boys come out through the doorway, neatly

dressed in western-style jackets. They notice Shanti Devi and rush towards her. She draws something on the stone stairs with a piece of chalk, which she has taken out of her bag.

"What is it?" asks Prabhash. "Shanti Devi, what are you doing?"

"Can't you see she's drawing," says Subhash. "She's drawing the temple."

Prabhash and Subhash are twins, the youngest sons of the distinguished and wealthy lawyer, Tara Chand Mathur. Tara Chand Mathur lives near Rang Bahadur Mathur and his family. Tara Chand Mathur and Rang Bahadur Mathur belong to the same caste.

Tara Chand Mathur is an esteemed and powerful gentleman who mixes in the finest social circles in New Delhi. In old Delhi there is nobody who lives better, dresses more elegantly, or who eats more delicious food than Tara Chand Mathur's family.

Tara Chand Mathur defends people in the highest court. He is known for his fearlessness. He says what he means to each and every one.

Perhaps it's a great honor for Shanti Devi to be able to play with Prabhash and Subhash, but she doesn't understand that.

"The drawing isn't true to life, Shanti Devi," says Prabhash. "It's too large. Our temple doesn't look like that."

Prabhash points and gesticulates, but Shanti Devi continues unconcerned and fills in detail after detail. The temple becomes far too large with a clocktower and spires and a gate which just grows and grows.

In flight

"That is not our temple," says Subhash. "Where is this temple?"

"It's the Real temple," explains Shanti Devi. "You have never seen it, but I often go there. The staircase is as lofty as it is here in my sketch."

The boys look awkwardly at each other.

"She imagines so many things," protests Prabhash. "That temple doesn't exist."

"Yes it does," says Shanti Devi. "I go there every day when I'm at home. It's the Dvarkadish temple in Muttra."

"Now she's talking about Muttra again," laughs Prabhash. "Dvarka, Dvarka ..." He can't pronounce the difficult word.

The greengrocer calls out in a hoarse voice from his rickety horsecart which is overloaded with pears, apples, grain and corn, treacle and syrup in glass bottles.

"Is there a town called Muttra?" asks Shanti Devi.

"Yes, there is such a town," he growls. "Everyone knows about it."

"Is it far away?" asks Shanti Devi.

The greengrocer rubs his chin. "About a day's journey, or perhaps two. It depends if one travels in a carriage or on foot ..."

"I want to go there," says Shanti Devi decidedly. "Please show me the way."

The greengrocer smiles amiably towards the irresistible face of the little girl. He picks up an apple and gives it to her.

"Here is something for you to eat on the way," he says. "You can continue straight on, only straight on."

He goes on his way in his horsecart. Shanti Devi watches him disappear into the distance. Then she picks up her bag and start walking slowly. Prabhash and Subhash follow after her.

"Come inside with us," they say, "so we can play in our large courtyard. There you can draw a new temple. You surely can't go to Muttra by yourself?"

"Oh yes I can," says Shanti Devi obstinately. "Nothing can prevent me. If I can only manage to get there, then I know that I'll be able to find my way home."

The twins follow her a while but they soon turn back. Shanti Devi continues alone. It was supposed to be straight forward, but the street starts to curve. A baker is sitting on a street corner.

"I want to go to Muttra," says Shanti Devi. "Which way is it to Muttra?"

"What are you going to do there?" asks the baker.

"I'm married there. My husband is waiting for me."

The baker bursts out laughing, but when he sees that Shanti Devi is offended, he changes his expression.

"Oh, you're married there? Happily married, I hope?"

"I am very happily married. My husband is a businessman, and he has a large store near the temple. He is no baker. ..."

Someone stops by the baker's small open street-shop and listens to what Shanti Devi is saying. Others come from the silk merchant opposite the baker's. Even more come from the turban merchant and band merchant. A rickshaw comes to a halt. There is a crowd of people.

Some ask questions. Shanti Devi answers hesitantly. Then people begin to laugh, not unkindly, but more as one who would laugh at a child. Shanti Devi's face becomes wet with tears.

She must get away from there. She runs as fast as her legs will carry her between the bazaars where material rustles, vessels clink and coins rattle on counters. Never again will she say anything to grown-ups—not even to children.

"Isn't that little Shanti Devi? Where are you going?"

Before her stands a large and impressive figure in a dark costume. It is Tara Chand Mathur, the lawyer. He is so tall that she has to bend her neck a long way backwards to be able to confront his friendly and amused glance. However, Tara Chand Mathur's friendliness is not false, she has sat in his lap. They are neighbors and friends. She puts her hands together on her chest in a gesture of greeting and makes a curtsey.

"*Namash te*, Tara Chand Mathur."

"*Namash te*, little Shanti Devi," says the lawyer. "What are you doing here?"

"Nothing."

"Come now. I know you trust me, Shanti Devi."

"I'm on my way home, Tara Chand Mathur."

"Home? But you are going in the wrong direction. Come along with me so that we can talk while we walk. Please hold my hand. Have you been crying?"

"No!"

Tara Chand Mathur strokes her cheek. She has her little hand in his large, secure grip. She feels calm and secure. Now nobody dares to laugh at her any more.

One who listened

"It was you who wanted to have a picture of Krishna. Have you received it?"

"Yes, thank you. I have and it makes me so happy. Sometimes I pray to him and he answers me."

"He answers you? Are you quite sure?"

"I believe so. In Muttra, the town where I live, there is the Dvarkadish temple and I go there every day. I also bathe in the river."

"No, Shanti Devi. You live here in Delhi. This is not Muttra."

"No, this is not Muttra. That's why I want to go home, but there is nobody who can show me how to get there. Would not ... Tara Chand Mathur be kind enough to show me?"

The lawyer is touched by the little girl with pigtails who is holding a suitcase and has such a serious face. He looks down at her.

"You've packed for the journey. What have you taken with you?"

"My jewelry and crayons, a shawl and some small things. At home I have everything I need. My chureys—they must be at home as well. I was given new ones before I ... before I became ill."

"Your chureys? That expression is not used here in Delhi. It means ankle bracelets."

"I had them when I danced, but when my legs started to hurt I couldn't dance any longer. My husband liked to see me dance. When we were newly-married I often danced."

"Your husband? You are married?"

"Yes, I'm married in Muttra."

The lawyer stops dead and studies Shanti Devi's soft but determined face.

This is unbelievable. This child can answer in such a way that one has a feeling of having discovered a pathway towards the truth. "What is actually going on in her little head?" he wonders.

"Does Tara Chand Mathur believe me? Tara Chand Mathur believes criminals who nobody else believes in. I'm just living here temporarily. I'm visiting. My name is not Shanti Devi. My name is Lugdi Devi."

"What's the name of your husband then?"

The girl hides her face in a fold of her sari. "I can't tell you that. My husband would not like me talking about him with strangers."

"Your husband would not like … You are really admirable, little Shanti Devi."

"Does Tara Chand Mathur believe in me? My husband is a highly respected businessman. He is extremely wealthy. He owns several houses and he loves me."

"If you tell me what your husband's name is, perhaps I might believe your story. We are no strangers, you and I, Shanti Devi. You also ought to give me the address of the house where you live in Muttra."

"Then I must ask my husband first. I can't tell you the address without being certain I'm allowed to tell you."

"How will you be able to ask him without first coming to Muttra? You do know the address?"

"Yes."

They walk quietly together towards Rang Bahadur's house. A little bit further away lives Tara Chand Mathur. The girl looks now and then searchingly at the lawyer as if waiting for an answer.

"Now you must go in to your nearest and dearest," says Tara Chand Mathur. "Perhaps we can arrange it so that you are able to travel to Muttra and meet your husband. Won't you be starting school shortly? How old are you?"

"Six years old. I'm starting school next year."

"Your husband would surely appreciate your being able to read, write and calculate when you come. He's a businessman, after all. Go in now. We may be able to help you."

Tara Chand Mathur goes inside his house but turns around in the doorway. Shanti Devi's face shines towards him. He feels almost ashamed.

When he's inside he immediately regrets what he has said. It was only to get rid of that persistent slip of a child. She'll forget the whole thing when she's a little older, he persuades himself.

However he can't free himself from thoughts about the girl.

When he tries to concentrate on the report of the proceedings from an important trial, he sees Shanti Devi gazing at him from page after page. What can he do in such a case?

Mod Mathi, his wife, stands in the doorway. It's time for dinner.

"You start to work as soon as you come home," she says. "You look worried. Have you been chosen to defend the nationalist leaders?"

"Yes, naturally," says Tara Chand Mathur, "but that doesn't worry me. I'm only wondering if a lawyer can take it upon himself to defend a little girl who believes she's reincarnated."

The mockery of friends

The Ramjas School is a school of excellent repute where one can learn English after completing primary school. Shanti Devi's parents are anxious to give her the best possible education available.

An Indian woman's place is in the home even in this day and age, but Shanti Devi's talent ought to make her a good match.

It's a hot day in September and the sun is high in the sky. This particular day the children finish school a little earlier than usual.

"Look! Shanti Devi! There goes Shanti Devi! *Mrs.* Shanti Devi!"

She doesn't even turn her head but hurries out onto the street.

"Mrs. Shanti Devi! Wait awhile; may we speak to the married Lady?"

The voices are from girls she recognizes—her fellow class companions. They can't mean to be so nasty, she persuades herself.

At this hour her father ought to be here in a rickshaw as he usually does, but she can't see him anywhere. He must have been delayed. He is always kind enough to pick her up after school. Perhaps he is afraid that something will happen to her.

"Do you know, she's not quite right in the head. Have you heard, she believes that she is married. Come on girls, let's go and speak to Shanti Devi."

The buzz of voices behind Shanti Devi grows louder. Why doesn't her father come to collect her?

"We just want to know how Mrs. Devi is feeling."

It's a boy's voice and she becomes seriously alarmed. A hand reaches out after her satchel. She pulls it back again but not so hard as to damage it. Three girls and two boys surround her.

"Isn't it your husband who usually comes to collect you, Shanti Devi? After all, you are married, aren't you?"

"Shame on you, Shanti Devi. A good housewife doesn't keep her husband waiting," one of the other school companions shout at her.

She doesn't want to begin to cry and let them triumph.

"Why are you doing this to me?" she says calmly. "I haven't done anything to hurt you."

"Won't you tell us what it's like to be married? Have you any children?

"Would you please be considerate. I have a long journey home," pleads Shanti Devi. "Let me go. Be careful with my bag."

"We won't allow her to go home, "says the boy wearing a tie. "We'll hold onto her until she has told us everything. Did you hear that, Shanti Devi?"

"I am married," says Shanti Devi as she struggles to hold back her tears. "It's true. You don't understand. I am another woman."

The girls giggle hysterically and the boy wearing the tie keeps them away with a commanding wave of his hand.

"She's someone else. Did you all hear that? This is most interesting and important. Who are you then?"

"I can't tell you that."

"If you won't tell us what your name is and where you live, we'll keep you here until it gets dark."

"Pull her hair," screams one of the girls. "Roll her in the grass. Confess! Are you lying?"

"No, I'm not lying. Leave me alone."

Shanti Devi's frail world has been affronted. She has been careless and told the girls her story a couple of times when they first met, and they haven't forgotten it. Now they want to show off in front of the older boys.

At the same moment, a man wearing the national costume comes up to them. The children move aside. It's Shanti Devi's head teacher, Bishan Chand.

"What are you doing? Why are you all so nasty towards such a little girl? You boys who are older ought to know better."

"It's not the boys' fault," says one of the girls ingratiatingly. "She is lying, sir. She says that she is married and extremely wealthy and that her husband is a Brahmin. We were just trying to teach her to tell the truth, sir."

The boy wearing the tie bows deeply.

"She started it. She didn't want to be together with us because her husband is so splendid."

"What rubbish you speak," exclaims the schoolmaster. "Go on home. You, Shanti Devi, what have you made up?"

The teacher's voice is impatient but it has a warm undertone. Shanti Devi sobs so that she can hardly utter a word.

"I haven't, I haven't ..."

"Come now, calm down my dear. What has happened?"

"They wanted me to confess that I'm lying, but I really am married to a businessman who lives in Muttra. Muttra is my Real home."

The teacher stares at her. One can't be too hard on such a slip of a girl, but there are limits.

"The most valuable thing of all is the truth," he says. "Have you heard about Sat-Chit-Ananda, truth, spirit and happiness? Without truth there is no spirit. Without spirit no happiness. Truth is life's foundation. Think about it while you walk home and don't let me hear any more talk about this. Children must play, but this is no child's play."

"I am a grown woman," explains Shanti Devi in sudden defiance.

"Then we will have to get to the bottom of this story. I must speak to your father. No, wait a little ... it was not my intention to frighten you. Don't run away."

She's not looking any longer for her father. She just keeps running, running. The teacher's voice haunts her. She hears the girls' giggle.

People stare at her. She catches a glimpse of them as if they were shadows. She must get away from here—away. She wants to escape from everyone who can't understand.

Lugdi Devi was my wife

"Lugdi Devi, you needn't be afraid. You'll soon be well again. You're being given the best possible care the doctors can give you at the hospital. My dearest doll … You'll soon be back in your beautiful home. Little doll, you'll only be leaving me for a short time. Lugdi Devi …"

She hears the familiar voice within. It's as if she is being stabbed with a sharp knife. The pain is unbearable.

"I would like my son to named Naunita, one who is enlightened by wisdom."

The well-known temple rises above her. It must be the Real temple. If she can only reach it she'll surely be rescued. Then nobody can hurt her, but she doesn't have enough strength; she's so tired …

"Krishna," she whispers, "please help me."

She experiences the façade ascending upwards shimmering in yellow and orange. There is the mighty bronze door. "Oh, Dvarkadish!"

No, it's not here. It's not a door that she recognizes. It is not the same temple. It's meaningless to search for something which doesn't exist.

"Who are you, child, who's lying here on the temple steps and crying?"

It's an unfamiliar voice, but it has a mildness which until now she has never heard. A hand strokes her hair with just a light touch. She experiences a feeling of great tenderness and warmth. She looks up into the smiling woman's face.

"Who are you?" asked the woman.

"I don't know," whispers Shanti Devi.

Maitri Devij, the holy mother

An unknown woman stands bent over her. She is completely dressed in orange. The woman sits beside Shanti Devi on the steps and draws her closer towards her. Shanti Devi becomes calm and happy.

"I must tell you," she says. "My name is Shanti Devi, but at the same time I know that I am also another woman whose name is Lugdi Devi. I am a child, but I am a real woman as well. I am grown-up. I was born here in Delhi, but I was also born in a town called Muttra. I am married there, I know the name of my husband and I also know the address where we live. At first I was confused and I didn't quite understand that it was myself. Then everything became clearer and clearer, I'm discovering more and more."

"I understand," says the woman. "It's very difficult. Are you suffering from it?"

"No, I don't know. I am not … ill."

"You mustn't prevent your recollections from appearing, nor must you force yourself to remember. Just allow your recollections to continue. There is no harm in that. You mustn't be upset about it."

"I have been extremely upset sometimes because I'm different from others. Do you believe me?"

"Yes, I believe you," says the smiling woman. "No, please don't cry now, Shanti Devi. You ought to be happy instead, now that you've found someone who believes you."

"Now I'm crying because I'm so happy. Who are you?"

"People call me the Mother," says the woman. "It's not my real name, but if someone says 'mother' to me, I listen to them. You understand, when people are destitute, they become as helpless as small children."

"Yes," says Shanti Devi, "I know. Can you please tell me how one can get to Muttra, mother?"

"If one stands with their back towards the Red Fort and one continues along Daryganj straight forward, Muttra is not difficult to find. But the road is dusty and long and a tiny body like yours couldn't possibly manage it. You'll have to wait until your body is strong enough. How old are you? Eight, nine?"

"I shall soon be nine years old. My parents, my present parents, live in Chirakhana not far from Chandni Chauk. My father's name is Rang Bahadur Mathur."

"I understand," says the woman. "Can that be your father over there, who is looking for you?"

Shanti Devi catches sight of a familiar figure. She waves and he immediately discovers her. He hurries up the steps and stands a bit away and bows reverently.

"Holy Mother, please forgive this foolish child who has disturbed your privacy with her chatter. Forgive me, I am this child's unhappy father. Please let me touch your feet. Bless this confused child and this man who does his very best to try and take care of his nearest and dearest."

"God bless you, Rang Bahadur," answers the woman.

"Don't be upset and afraid. This child is innocent and guiltless. Her [karmic] debt is small."

"I understand that she has told you everything. She can never learn to hold her tongue. Shouldn't she be able to keep things to herself? Is it not written in the *Vedas* that he who remembers his previous lives must die?"

"He who forgives all, also forgives her. Don't brood any more over the Law, but go home instead, Rang Bahadur."

The woman in orange touches Rang Bahadur's head with her hand and thereafter Shanti Devi's head. Then she leaves them. Shanti Devi watches her go with a wistful expression on her face.

"Who is she?"

"That is the Holy Mother, Maitri Deviji," answers Rang Bahadur. "She is very good and very wise. Let's go now."

"I want to stay here. Soon the procession will arrive. I remember the drums, pipes and string instruments. It's exactly the same as it is in Muttra. You mustn't prevent me from seeing the procession."

You have convinced me

The walls of the temple turn red in the sunset. The heat subsides.

Lamps are lit. Flames from small fires rise up from the alleyways. The jingle of the pakhawaj, the whining of the sitar, the dull tone of the sarod is mingled with blazing colors. The elephants bear flower-covered steeples on their backs. Elephants with gold-plated mouthpieces are decorated with embroidered saddle cloths. The ceremonious procession advances in the rapidly falling twilight.

"It's Navaratra," says Rang Bahadur. "It's the Durga festival which goes on for nine days and nights."

"Father, I was married during Navaratra in Muttra," says Shanti Devi. "It was as beautiful then as it is now, perhaps even more beautiful. My husband rode himself, together with the others in the procession, on a white horse and he collected me from the house of the Chaturbhujs."

"Chaturbhuj? You've never mentioned that name before."

"Chaturbhuj was my father in Muttra. My mother's name is Jagti. My husband collected me and let me ride together with him in the procession. We were so young and we loved each other. I was wearing a white sari, my wedding sari. It was covered with pearls, all in white. My husband was wearing a long embroidered shervani and a yellow turban. My jewelry was very expensive."

"What is the name of your husband."

"You know I'm not allowed to tell you. I must ask him first."

"Can you describe his appearance?"

"Why must I describe his appearance? I would recognize him among a thousand men. He has a mustache."

"There are so many men who have a mustache. Can't you tell me anything else?"

"He has a birthmark on his cheek. He is somewhat embarrassed about it."

Rang Bahadur watches the girl thoughtfully. How many times has he not studied her in secret to try to get an idea of what she is thinking about—who she really is.

"If I could only understand where you get everything from which you maintain you have seen before. Sometimes I believe . . ."

"What do you believe, father?"

"You have convinced me, Shanti Devi. I don't want to admit it myself, but I must be honest. There is something about you that can't be explained in a normal manner. I admit it, Shanti Devi."

"You make me so happy, father."

"You are no child, even though you have a child's body, Shanti Devi. I'm speaking to you as a grown-up. If the truth is meant to be known, then nobody can prevent it."

A visit

It's the ninth night of the Navaratra celebrations. All the processions have now passed, all the images are burned. Now that the much longed for festival is over, the streets and alleyways are empty in Chirakhana. If someone comes, it can be heard in the distance. Dry leaves crackle under their feet.

"They're not going to open the door. Yes, they are. I can hear steps."

The knocking on the door ceases. The two gentlemen are invited into Rang Bahadur's house.

"Namash te, Rang Bahadur Mathur. We are from the Ramjas School where your daughter Shanti Devi is a pupil. I am the headmaster Lala Chand and this is Shanti's form master, Bishan Chand."

"What can I do for you gentlemen?"

"We are here with the best of intentions, Rang Bahadur. We would like to speak to you about your daughter, Shanti Devi."

The Headmaster is a corpulent, jovial man with a halo of white hair under a Gandhi cap.

"Shanti Devi has given us much anxiety," says Rang Bahadur. "You know what she's like."

"She is a well-behaved and conscientious girl," says the Headmaster. "She is one of the best in her class."

The Form master nods in agreement.

"She always does her homework most satisfactorily," he says. "I have no complaints against her, Rang Bahadur."

"That's not what I mean," says her father. "It's just that she has so many ideas and strange thoughts. We are unable to quieten her. She talks about such things which a child ought not know about."

"I frightened her the other day unintentionally," says the Form master. "I've given much thought to her behavior. She is an extremely interesting girl."

"She talks about this and that. One day she says one thing, another day she says something quite different."

"We have discussed Shanti Devi's case and we feel her statements are quite logical. I have devoted a great deal of attention to the theory of reincarnation. I would be grateful if you would allow me to ask her some questions," says the Headmaster.

Rang Bahadur opens the door to the inner room. Shanti Devi is sitting up straight on her bed and looks at him with large, dark eyes. He beckons her to wrap a shawl around herself.

The Form master nods encouragingly towards her.

"We have come to speak to you about your previous life." Shanti Devi blushes. She is dismayed yet at the same time happy. Her heart beats heavily.

"My previous life?" she stammers.

"Yes, does it not feel as if you have a life before this present life? You've lived in another town. You grew up there; you've had a home there. You so want it to continue, but it doesn't and you must try and understand what has happened. How do you comprehend all this? Is it as if you see pictures in front of you?"

"I see pictures and I hear voices," says Shanti Devi excitedly. "When I want to see, it becomes clearer. Then it's as if I'm actually there. A yellow house with beautiful windows. We live there and we are very happy. My husband talks to me. He is a Brahmin. One morning before he went to his store, which is situated near the Dvarkadish's temple, I heard that he went into my prayer room and asked Krishna for a son. I am sad. Perhaps I'll never have a son. My Jeth (brother-in-law) comforts me by the well. I am so young. There are so many pictures, so many voices. I'm crying. I'm lying in bed and am so tired and I'm in so much pain. The pain doesn't get better, it becomes dark."

Both men look at the girl with surprise. Now even her voice sounds different than it usually does. It's more mature and has another intonation.

"I often walked to the temple and bathed in the Jumna. When I had a pain in my foot, a servant waited for me in a rickshaw. We are driving through the Great gate, Krishna's gate. The street is blue. My husband is extremely generous and kind. I'm unhappy when he leaves me. Once he left me when I was terribly ill and was about to be taken to a hospital in a town which, I don't remember the name of. Perhaps I'll remember it if I search my memory."

"What happened there?" asks the Headmaster.

Shanti Devi has tears in her eyes. "I can't remember."

"But you name was Lugdi Devi?" asks Lala Chand. "Where did you live?"

"We lived on the street named after the Chaubeys. The ninth house on Chaubey Street in Muttra."

"I haven't heard her say that before, "exclaims Rang Bahadur. "That's the address?"

"Yes," says Shanti Devi humbly. "That's where my home was." The Headmaster and Form master exchange glances, while Rang Bahadur looks down at the floor.

The Headmaster Lala Chand has a feeling that they must now be extremely careful and not ask too much.

"We've heard enough for now," says the Headmaster. "You don't remember the name of your husband, do you? And it's none of our business anyway."

"We were married during the festival of Navaratra," whispers Shanti Devi. "It was our wedding, our wedding night."

"It's a pity you can't remember your husband's name," says the Headmaster. "Still, you know so many other things."

"His name is Kedar Nath," whispers the girl.

She covers her face with her hands. When Rang Bahadur trys to hug her and calm her down, she pulls away. She goes back into the bedroom without giving the three men further thought.

The Headmaster's letter

"She must have experienced it," says Lala Chand. "The whole of her personality is characterized by these memories. How otherwise is it possible that a child can seize names and details out of the air in the way that she does? Now one ought to take her to Muttra as soon as possible so that her information can be correctly verified."

"Does this Kedar Nath Chaubey exist?" wonders Bishan Chand. "We must find out if there really is someone with that name."

Rang Bahadur assumes a negative attitude.

"Gentlemen, you may do whatever you consider appropriate. We, Shanti Devi's parents, don't want to do anything which may jeopardize her future. It's generally thought that it is dangerous to delve into such matters."

"It is perhaps even more dangerous not to delve into it," remarks the Headmaster. "Surely, you must also be anxious to know how matters stand?"

"I will not allow it," says Rang Bahadur firmly. "The girl must not be used in any experiment. You have no right ..."

"We naturally have no right," says Lala Chand with a disarming smile. "We understand so well how you feel. Perhaps the journey can be postponed until sometime in the future."

"That sounds better. Then she'll have time to grow up and be more sensible," says Rang Bahadur. "She'll have time to become more stable."

Both men say goodbye and go on their way.

Out on the street they pass a teahouse which is open. Lala Chand slows down.

"Let's go inside," he says. "I have an idea." A bearded sikh bows and comes up to their table with tea and rice cakes. The Headmaster asks for paper and a pencil.

"You're going to write to him?" exclaims the Form master. "But we don't know if he exists."

"Then we'll know," answers Lala Chand. "One can always trust the post office. If he doesn't exist, then there will be no answer."

He writes in elegant handwriting:

Pandit Kedar Nath Chaubey
Chaubey street 9
Mathura

Most honored Sir!

I have come into contact with a girl whose name is Shanti Devi Mathur and who lives in Chirakhana, Delhi. She is the daughter of businessman, Rang Bahadur Mathur. She is able to recall information about you which is astonishing. This is what she says: "In my past life I was a Chaubey from Mathura. My caste was that of a brahmin and my husband's name was Kedar Nath. He had a store near the Dvarkadish temple. The color of my house was yellow. The name I had then was Lugdi Devi."

May I trouble you, pandit, to be kind enough and inform me if there is indeed any truth in these statements? Has Lugdi Devi existed? Does Kedar Nath exist? Please write to me if you exist!

With God's blessings and with the greatest humility.

Lala Kishan Chand
Headmaster, The Ramja School, Darygani, Delhi.

"I find it difficult to believe that there will be any outcome," says the Form master. "Brahmins of the old school are extremely reserved."

"Don't forget that he is a businessman," says the Headmaster. "He must be used to dealing with people. I have a strong feeling that we will receive an answer."

Kedar Nath's answer

Days and weeks go by, life continues in the normal way.

One day in the school playground the Headmaster calls out to his colleague, Bishan Chand. His jovial face exhibits an expression of triumph. He takes a letter out of his pocket and reads out loud:

Headmaster Lala Kishan Chand
The Ramja School
Daryganj, Delhi

I was extremely surprised, not to mention how excited I felt when I received your letter. What you have written is absolutely correct. I have had a wife whose name was Lugdi Devi. She is deceased. I do have a store which is near the Dvarkadish temple

Who is this little girl who knows all this?

I have a cousin in Delhi whose name is pandit Kanji Mal. He is employed by a company named Messrs. Bhasa Mal & Gulzarri Mal. I have at the present time written to him and asked him to contact you immediately. I would be extremely grateful if you could arrange it so that he can meet the girl in a suitable manner.

May Krishna love and protect us all, everywhere.

Kedar Nath Chaubey

The Form master is speechless at first. He has to read the letter several times before he is quite convinced. He has no objections to make. What Shanti Devi has said is true and not just fantasies.

"My intuition, has from the very beginning, been telling me that the girl was right," mumbles the Form master," but I've tried to fight against it so as not to be regarded as altogether too gullible. Now we must overcome the parent's resistance."

"What does it matter about their resistance now?" says the Headmaster. Both men walk back and forth in the playground during the discussion. The lessons are finished for the day.

On the nearest side of the street there isn't much traffic. A horse carriage approaches and stops outside the entrance to the school. A man they don't recognize gets out. He introduces himself politely.

"I am Kanji Mal Chaubey, Kedar Nath Chaubey's cousin. I'm looking for the Headmaster Lala Kishan Chand with regard to a letter which I have received from Muttra."

"I am Lala Kishan Chand."

"It's an extraordinary letter about a little girl whose name is Shanti Devi. She maintains that she is Kedar Nath's reincarnated wife, Lugdi Devi. Do you know this girl?"

"Yes, she is a student here at the school," answers the Headmaster. "You knew Lugdi Devi naturally?"

"I have lived for several years in Muttra and knew her very well. May I meet the girl?"

"Her parents are quite adverse to it. They fear that their child can come to some harm. You must be extremely careful. It's best if you go by yourself so that nobody can influence you. I will give you the address to

Rang Bahadur's house."

"On the other hand, it would be most interesting even for us to see how the girl reacts," says the Form master. "We may never have the opportunity of witnessing such a meeting again."

On his way there Kanji Mal thinks about Lugdi Devi as he remembers her, so incredibly beautiful, a very special almost saint-like woman.

"How can this Shanti Devi know anything about Lugdi Devi's personal relationships? She is not even nine years old," mutters Kanji Mal to himself.

When he gets out of the horse carriage it's with the distinct feeling that his mission just now is to help his cousin reveal forgery.

How is my son?

The door is open. Kanji Mal and both the teachers walk into the open, light courtyard.

Kanji Mal glances at a flight of stairs. He notices a woman and a little girl who is standing above them and watching him with large, expressive eyes.

"Mama," she says, "a gentleman has come to visit."

"It must be a business acquaintance who's come to see your father. I don't recognize him."

"But I do, mama; I recognize him."

Kanji Mal looks up surprised. The girl jumps down the stairs and puts her arms around his legs. She clings firmly to him. He would like to stroke her hair, but he controls himself.

"Do you recognize me? It's impossible."

"I know for certain that I recognize you, but I can't remember your name. You are my husband's cousin."

Kanji Mal looks petrified and doesn't know what to say. The others who are present are also quiet.

"How can you know that I am your husband's cousin

if you don't know my name?" stammers Kanji Mal.

"I recognize you. You have only changed a little. You have become … more of a stranger. You are larger and stronger somehow. You are Kedar Nath's younger cousin."

"Kedar Nath's?"

"Yes, that is my husband. He is a businessman in Muttra. You lived with us when I was Lugdi Devi. Don't you still live in Muttra?"

Kanji Mal wipes his forehead.

"I have moved," he says. "I wasn't allowed …"

"You had difficulty trying to find a home you liked and that was why you wanted to live with us. I remember more and more now. You didn't want to work for Kedar Nath because you wanted to be independent. Have you married yet?"

"Married? No."

Kanji Mal's arguments have already fallen apart. The little girl looks at him with such an open and affectionate expression that he feels he must now stroke her hair.

"I should very much like to ask her some questions."

"Just please remember that she is just a child."

"Of course. Do you remember how many brothers your husband Kedar Nath had?"

The girl nods. "My husband only has one brother."

"Was he older or younger than your husband?"

"Older, of course. He's my Jeth. Is he still alive?"

Jeth is a dialectic expression for an older brother, which Lugdi Devi usually used.

"He's alive and well. When you were Lugdi Devi, was Kedar Nath's father, your father-in-law, still alive?"

"Yes, he was, but he was rather frail and was in much pain. How is he now?"

"He's greatly improved. Would you recognize him

as well?"

"Naturally. I would recognize everybody, almost everybody."

That was a wise reservation. Because if one has been away for a long period of time not all faces are so easy to recognize.

Kanji Mal studies Shanti Devi, as if he hopes to find characteristic features similar to those of Lugdi Devi, but he can see no external resemblance.

"Where did you live in Muttra?" he continues thoughtfully. "Oh yes, I know that already from the letter."

Shanti Devi looks bewildered.

"You gave us the address," says the headmaster. "We sent a letter to your husband so we could verify your statement."

The girl lowers her head.

"You shouldn't have done that," she whispers. "What will my husband think now? I regret telling you his name. Perhaps he'll take offense. Maybe I won't be allowed to travel to Muttra again."

"Your husband wrote to his cousin. I hope you're happy that he's come to see you."

"Yes, very happy. Now I remember your name. You are Kanji Mal Chaubey."

A revelation

She controls herself and looks pleadingly up towards the man from Muttra.

"Then Kedar Nath already knows everything. Why is it he doesn't come and get me? These parents are good and kind and I like them, but please, Kanji Mal, take me back to Muttra."

She clings to him. In the glances which are exchanged between Prem Pyari and Rang Bahadur he catches a glimpse of despair. Now he must try to express himself diplomatically.

"Your husband is occupied with business," he answers. "At the present time he doesn't have time to receive you."

"But he hasn't forgotten Lugdi Devi?"

"How could anyone forget Ludgi Devi? Nobody can forget her. She was the most wonderful woman."

"Did they still like her after she'd gone?"

"Everybody liked her, including myself."

Shanti Devi looks at him with a faint smile.

"You were particularly fond of Lugdi Devi," she says. "She was your cousin's wife but you would never admit it. Perhaps you liked her more than you ought to have. She understood that. Once you came so near to her ... I remember."

"No, no!" interrupts Kanji Mal. "There are things one shouldn't talk about." He seems suddenly completely shaken. Shanti Devi has a proud expression on her small, childish face.

"It's you who ask, not I. What else would you like to know? I lived in a yellow house and nearby there was a grocery shop. I did the shopping myself so that I could see the goods. When I was ill the servants did it. Then it cost more money."

"Lugdi Devi was extremely generous," says Kanji Mal. "Didn't she let people borrow money? Didn't she often give money away?"

"Yes, she was extravagant in that way. She had a little money hidden in a secret place at home which nobody else but herself knew about. It was on the top floor. There was 150 rupees there which she should have given to my Dvarkadish temple as an offering. When I come to my Real home I shall point the place out. Nobody but myself knows about it. Perhaps my husband also knows about it."

"Why were you going to offer that money?"

"I prayed to Krishna for a son. I did get the boy we longed for and I named him Launita Lal. After ten days I became terribly ill. I had been ill the whole time, but then it became so difficult. I don't quite remember ..."

"What happened?" asks Kanji Mal with a trembling voice.

Shanti Devi hides her face in her hands. When she looks up again she doesn't have any tears in her eyes. Her gaze is calm and clear.

"I died," she says.

It becomes cold immediately, even though the sun is shining.

"Do you remember where you ... where you died?"

"I was taken to a hospital in a large town which I have tried to remember the name of. I was so tired and was in great pain. Sometimes everything became dark. I laid in bed and prayed to Krishna. I knew that I had given birth to a son. When my husband was happy I was happy as well."

Kanji Mal can't prevent his tears from running down his cheeks. He kisses the girl gently on her forehead.

"Lugdi Devi," he whispers tenderly. "Little Lugdi Devi ..."

He walks toward the door and thanks Shanti Devi's parents. Everyone is touched by this strange meeting.

"I came here as a skeptic and I'm leaving as a believer," said Kanji Mal. "I am convinced. In this frail girl's body lives Lugdi Devi's spirit. Lugdi Devi is with us again."

He opens the door and walks away. Shanti Devi

dashes after him.

"I would just like to ask you—how is my son?"

Kanji Mal stops and lifts her up.

"Your son is healthy and strong. He's a splendid boy who's well developed. He's a little larger than you are yourself."

Shanti Devi meets her beloved

Mathura or Muttra is Krishna's holy town. It is said that there are to be found no less than a thousand temples in honor of the Savior of India.

Kedar Nath Chaubey's store is on the Vishrant Ghat. He buys and sells material and other goods. Kedar Nath is a tall, well-built man with a fine sculptured face.

This particular morning he is deeply disconcerted by a letter which arrived from Delhi.

Dear Cousin,

I have visited the girl Shanti Devi and found that she is the deceased Lugdi Devi. She remembers everything about her previous life and what happened in Muttra. She has totally convinced me. I would suggest you come here and meet her yourself.

Your affectionate Cousin,

Kanji Mal

Kedar Nath has succeeded in pushing aside his feelings for his deceased wife, his longing for her and his grief, but now everything has been brought to life again.

However, he has made his decision. He will travel to Delhi with his present wife and his and Lugdi Devi's son. Perhaps the girl would like to see her son from her previous life, Naunita Lal, who is Kedar Nath's pride and joy.

But how is he going to be able to explain to his wife what has happened to them? She has the usual conception of life but is a good and affectionate wife.

Compared to Lugdi Devi she is perhaps rather colorless, but how can one expect a quite ordinary woman to be comparable to Lugdi Devi, who was almost like a saint?

He smiles faintly at the thought of Lugdi Devi and it doesn't trouble him any longer to think about her.

Are you Lugdi Devi?

Kedar Nath thinks about Kanji Mal and wonders nevertheless if his cousin hasn't allowed himself to be convinced far too easily.

Even if other men, yes, even his own cousin, are naive enough to let themselves be convinced on flimsy grounds, he doesn't need to do so himself.

Kedar Nath has his plan ready. He will arrive disguised. The girl will truly be put to the test. She must definitely submit evidence which none other than Kedar Nath himself can possibly know about. Only then can he believe her.

Rang Bahadur's house is festively decorated with flags and garlands. They always do this when they are about to receive neighbors and friends in Delhi.

Little Shanti Devi also takes part in the party. She eats rice and fruit with well-poised gestures. She is a real little lady.

Then the door opens and a man enters. He is wearing an embroidered costume. It is obviously a distinguished gentleman. The ladies quickly cover their heads with the ends of their saris.

Rang Bahadur and Prem Pyari hurry forward and welcome their guest. He bends his head slightly and holds his right hand diagonally pointing upwards over his chest.

"I am babu Ram Chaubey from Mathura, and was sent here by my brother, Kedar Nath Chaubey. May I have a few minutes of your time, even though you have guests?"

"You are welcome as our guest," says Rang Bahadur.

Shanti Devi looks at the guest with large, shining eyes. Her face is as white as a sheet. Her lips are trembling. She captures the man's glance and manages to hold it awhile. Then she pulls up her sari and hides her face in it.

"It's about your daughter," says the guest. "My brother has received a letter regarding an extraordinary occurrence and he has become interested. He doesn't have time to come himself, so he has sent me here instead to prevent unnecessary rumors."

"Couldn't you have chosen a more suitable time?" wonders Prem Pyari. "We have had difficulties with our daughter."

"I don't want to offend anyone," says the guest with unexpected softness. "I am only seeking the truth."

"You are already a guest in our house," says Rang Bahadur. "You would like to meet our daughter, Shanti Devi? I assume."

"Yes, indeed, so that's her name. Is it the girl over there? Why is she hiding her face?"

"She's shy. Shanti Devi, we have a new guest who would like to talk to you. He is from Muttra and his name is babu Ram Chaubey."

The girl looks up from her sari with an expression in

her large eyes which none of the onlookers will ever forget.

"You are not my Jeth," she says. "You are Kedar Nath!"

"Yes, yes, I am Kedar Nath," answers the other. "It's true. O good God, it's true."

He stares at the child as if he has lost possession of his senses. The guests begin to understand that an extraordinary drama is taking place. The silence creates a sentimental atmosphere.

"You still have your birthmark," says the girl with a little smile, "and the mustache of course. You are not much older. You are just as I remember you."

"Are you … Are you Lugdi Devi?" stammers Kedar Nath.

Shanti Devi stands dead silent and observes the man who has been her husband. Then the door opens and one of the guests lets in a little boy. Shanti Devi glances towards him. She runs towards him and throws her arms around him.

"My son," she exclaims, "my beloved Naunita Lal. It's me, your mother …"

"You are not my mother," protests the boy and tries to free himself.

She releases him, runs back to Kedar Nath and cries in desperation with her face pressed against his body. Kedar Nath is as perplexed as everyone else.

Then the boy comes back again, her son from the past. He is somewhat larger than Shanti Devi. He kneels beside Shanti Devi and tries to comfort her. Now he doesn't turn away when she embraces him.

She cries more violently than ever and Naunita Lal also begins to cry. What secret chords that are vibrating between them nobody knows.

"I remember everything," she exclaims. "I remember what it was like in the dark. I remember how I died ..."

Even Kedar Nath kneels down beside her and cautiously touches her hands. She greedily captures his hand in both of her hands.

"I have waited for you for such a long time," she whispers. "You came at last ..."

"It's so difficult," he says. "What shall I do? You must not cry anymore. You must be happy."

"That's exactly what you used to say when I was ill. You always wanted to make me happy, Kedar Nath. Have you kept the promise you made me?"

"What have I promised?"

"On my deathbed you promised me you would never get married again."

I forgive you

Whispers of astonishment are heard all around the room.

"I could not keep that promise," says Kedar Nath in a low voice. "I was a man in his prime; it was impossible. I did not mean to break the promise then, I swear, Lugdi Devi, but I just couldn't keep it. My present wife is a homely woman, but she is a good wife and a good mother."

"You don't need to explain," says Shanti Devi. "Lugdi Devi, who is a part of me, forgives you. I'm not asking for anything, only that you are happy. I'm so happy to be able to meet you and to see my son."

"I can't explain what I feel," whispers Kedar Nath. "Everything has been turned upside-down. I am helpless against something which I don't understand. I admit that

I wanted to forget Lugdi Devi. You are only a child."

Shanti Devi nods her head in resignation.

"I have a child's body. I am also helpless, but I am so happy to see that Naunita Lal is thriving. I was so weak." She now has tears in her eyes again. "Perhaps I wasn't much larger then than I am now. I was quite tiny and the child was large. Do you remember the picture of Krishna I had by my bedside at the hospital in Agra? Did you offer those 150 rupees as a sacrifice as I asked you to do if I gave birth to a son?"

"The 150 rupees?" repeats Kedar Nath questioningly. "I don't remember—it's such a long time ago. I ... I believe I forgot it. There was such a rush with the funeral and everything."

He suddenly stops speaking.

"Why was there such a rush with my funeral?" asks Shanti Devi.

She stops speaking and sits with a distant look in her eyes. Her face becomes completely white.

Prem Pyari wants to go up to Shanti Devi, but her husband stops her.

"Its gone far enough now. Nobody can do anything more for her than the man who is sitting beside her. You and I don't belong to our little girl any longer."

Shanti Devi hears his voice.

"You are my father," she whispers. "I don't deny it. Mother, would you please fetch some toys? I would like to play with my son."

Her mother fetches Shanti Devi's dolls and some playingcards. Shanti Devi lets her marionette dolls pull and shake in fits and starts.

Then they play with the cards which have gods, heroes and demons illustrated on them. It's a strange and enchanting scene. Kedar Nath watches fascinated by it.

"I like her so much, father," Naunital Lal calls out. "I just don't understand though how she can be my mother."

Now a new visitor, who is out of breath, comes into the room, lawyer Tara Chand Mathur. Rang Bahadur welcomes him heartily.

"Tara Chand Mathur, a miracle has happened. Kedar Nath Chaubey has come from Muttra and Shanti Devi has identified him as her husband in her previous life in the presence of all these witnesses."

"I am completely overwhelmed," says Kedar Nath. "This little girl is not like my deceased wife to look at, but I see Lugdi Devi's soul in her glance."

The rumor spreads quickly in Chirakhana. In no time at all there is a crowd of people outside Rang Bahadur's house. Everyone wants to see the Brahmin and his reincarnated child-wife.

You were unfaithful to me

After this first meeting with Shanti Devi Kedar Nath has returned to the hotel where he is staying with his family. However, everybody knows that he will be visiting Shanti Devi again.

When the taxicab arrives with Kedar Nath and his son there are so many people that it has great dfficulty making its way through the crowds.

As soon as he is inside the house and has shut the door behind him, Shanti Devi scampers up to him. He lifts her up and kisses her on the forehead, but she notices immediately that his manner is reserved.

"During the course of the evening, I've been thinking through the events which occurred yesterday in great detail," he says to Shanti Devi's father. "To be quite honest, I must admit that I have partly changed my opinion. The girl has not told me anything more than what she could have been told by people who knew Lugdi Devi. There is, after all, a possibility that the whole thing could have been arranged. It's true that she did recognize me, but someone could have described my appearance for her.

The promise at the deathbed which she made reference to, could have been a guess which just happened to be perfectly correct. Such promises are made quite often between two parties in difficult situations, whereby the one party's intentions are not as serious as the other's."

Shanti Devi's eyes now have a more fervent expression.

"I'm sorry you feel that way," says Rang Bahadur. "I'm afraid I must ask you to leave us immediately."

"I'm only searching for the truth," says Kedar Nath.

"You are as suspicious as you were before," says Shanti Devi and strokes his hand. "You have no respect for that which is sacred and don't believe that anyone else has either. But I'm going to give you evidence that nobody else can."

Kedar Nath hesitates when the girl speaks to him as if she were a grown woman, as Lugdi Devi would have done.

"Nobody can deny me the right to receive concrete evidence," he mumbles. "It's not being nasty ..."

"You were often cowardly and scared, Kedar Nath," says Shanti Devi. "I remember quite clearly how you behaved. My dear present parents, please be kind enough to leave us alone."

Rang Bahadur and Prem Pyari leave them. Shanti Devi pulls Kedar Nath towards her. They sit on a bench out in the courtyard.

"Can anyone have told me about the 150 rupees I wanted to sacrifice for my son?" asks Shanti Devi.

"I don't know where Lugdi Devi's hiding places are," he mumbles.

"You were extremely economical in some ways, Kedar Nath. Outwardly you were hospitable and generous, but when your wife asked for something you were often economical. Lugdi Devi, who is within me, loves you dearly, but she knows your weaknesses. She admires you, obeys you, is faithful to you, but have you always been faithful to Lugdi Devi?"

Kedar Nath is dismayed. "Naturally."

"It's not true. You were convinced that Lugdi Devi didn't know anything about it. When she became ill you were often impatient. She had to yield herself to you even though she was in such pain. You were a temperamental man and you almost forced yourself upon her. She couldn't manage it in the normal way without placing herself in a special position …"

Kedar Nath shrinks back and stares at her in horror.

"Stop, stop. I don't want to hear any more," he interposed. "There was no shame in it. How can you know about that?"

"Do you believe this then? There came a day when I just wasn't able to do as you wished. Then you began to look for another woman. You admired the nurse from Aligarh who was to take care of me several weeks before I was taken to the hospital."

"I don't know what you're talking about," exclaims Kedar Nath. "I don't remember that."

His cheeks are burning and he is extremely shocked.

"I remember every detail in Lugdi Devi's life, because I am Lugdi Devi. The girl from Aligarh was a very beautiful Anglo-Indian with pale skin. She was respectful towards me, but you would look at each other on the sly. You didn't think that I saw you exchange glances. The servants carried me out to the well. One day you didn't come out and see me even though you knew I was waiting for you out there. You didn't think I was able to walk by myself and the servants weren't at home. I called out, but you pretended not to hear me. Do you know why I couldn't walk?"

"You were pregnant. You were in great pain."

"Several years earlier when I was on a pilgrimage to Hardvar a bone splinter became stuck in my foot. It had wandered upwards in my leg. The doctors didn't understand what had happened. I didn't see a real doctor either; not until I came to the Lady Lyall's hospital in Agra and was operated on before I gave birth to my child. They didn't believe that I would be able to give birth in the normal way if they didn't operate."

"Lugdi Devi, forgive me ... Lugdi Devi, I loved you." Kedar Nath's tears begin to flow.

"That time at the well when you didn't think I was able to stand up, I did manage to somehow. It made my leg hurt dreadfully. In spite of the pain I moved quietly and hobbled into the house, leaning against the walls. I felt like an aged woman. Instead of having my lovely gold and red sari on, I was wrapped up in shawls like an old woman. In the room beyond I saw you and the girl, but you were far too engrossed in each other to notice me."

Kedar Nath's face is struck with terror.

"I didn't know ... I didn't believe. Lugdi Devi never said a word. Since that day ... Since that day she never spoke to me very much. How she must have suffered, my poor wife. She didn't say anything ..."

"She was heartbroken, but she didn't accuse. It would have been better if you had confronted her with it face to face."

"Oh, I can never make amends for what I've done! However long I may live and whatever I do I can never make amends."

He is shaking with sobs. Shanti Devi cautiously lays her hand on his arm to comfort him.

"It's too late, Kedar Nath," she says, "but Lugdi Devi, who is part of me, still loves you."

Her strength deserts her. She begins to cry as the child she is in the grown man's arms. He is shaken to the core, but it gives him comfort to be able to comfort her.

Rang Bahadur and his wife discover them. Deeply moved they listen to Kedar Nath's words.

"Everything that Shanti Devi has said is correct. I swear it, in the name of Krishna. Nobody can have any doubts. Lugdi Devi has returned."

The following day Kedar Nath Chaubey travels home to Muttra again together with his son and his wife. In spite of everything that has been said, he leaves Shanti Devi behind, according to the decision which has been made in consultation with her parents.

If the girl were to follow them to Muttra now and then later on travel there now and then, the consequences could be intolerable. Legally she is still Rang Bahadur's not-quite-nine-year-old daughter.

Kedar Nath arrived in Delhi on November 13, 1935, and travelled back home again on November 15th.

When Shanti Devi realizes that Kedar Nath has returned home and left her behind, she becomes completely apathetic and indifferent towards the world around her. She stops speaking to her family.

Her parents are in despair. However, after several days the crisis passes. Shanti Devi is once again calm and controlled.

One evening lawyer Tara Chand Mathur comes to Shanti Devi's home together with two gentlemen who are regarded as Delhi's most respected citizens.

They are the chairman of the publishers' association, Lala Deshbandu Gupta and politician Neki Ram Sharma, who is a personal friend of Mahatma Gandhi.

"Tara Chand Mathur has told me about your daughter," says Lala Deshbandu Gupta. "The newspapers print such exaggerated stories about this or that. There can be an unhealthy spreading of rumors. I suggest that an impartial committee of enquiry take the girl to Mathura and verify her statements in the aforesaid neighborhood and place."

"That is a sensible suggestion," says Tara Chand Mathur. "What is your opinion, Rang Bahadur?"

"Shanti Devi's husband from her previous life has been here, and also her husband's cousin. In their opinion her information corresponds with their own."

"Do you refuse to allow her to be taken to Mathura?" asks Neki Ram Sharma.

"Absolutely," answers Rang Bahadur.

Mahatma Gandhi intervenes

Who is the little man in the loincloth who is walking along Chirakhanas' narrow streets, respectfully followed by three distinguished gentlemen? He has a thin, almost shrivelled-up face. His head is totally bald and he doesn't have many teeth left, but his face is wreathed in wonderful smiles which he gives freely and good-heartedly to everyone. People everywhere admire and love him because of his strong passion for righteousness, truth and freedom.

Someone whispers that he is making his way to Rang Bahadur's house. Is it his intention to meet that strange girl?

People are prostrating themselves in the street and stretching out their hands trying to touch his feet.

"Is he not everyone's friend and father? Babu Gandiji, bless us!"

Gandhi laughs. He looks mild, almost innocent behind his thick spectacles. He waves his hand, as it is his intention that the people should get up again.

He does not want to be worshipped as a holy man or saint.

Gandhi's message is *ahimsa*, victory without the use of violence. One can win the hardest heart with humbleness and humility. He has developed the philosophy of non-violence from the science of yoga. Untruthfulness is over-come by not cooperating with it.

Gandhi meant that nothing permanent can be built with the help of violence. Violence only creates more violence. He goes so far in his definition of nonviolence as to say that a man should not even think negative thoughts about others.

A dirty boy without a caste runs towards him. Some-one tries to push the boy away, but Gandhi grabs hold of him and kisses him. The crowd cheers.

"It's here," says Neki Ram Sharma. "Let's go in."

Mahatma Gandhi ascends the dark staircase, followed by Neki Ram Sharma, Lala Deshbandu Gupta and Tara Chand Mathur.

Prem Pyari cannot believe her eyes when she is about to receive her guests. Rang Bahadur is dumbfounded. What an honor!

Gandhi smiles warmly and beckons Shanti Devi to come forward.

"This is the girl, I assume. So intelligent and mature for her age. I like her immediately," he says.

Rang Bahadur falls on his knees before the Mahatma and touches his feet.

"To what do I owe the honor of your visit?"

"It's about your child, Shanti Devi. Neki Ram Sharma has told me the incredible story. I would like you, Rang Bahadur, to allow the girl to travel to Muttra."

"I'm afraid that she will be unhappy in the future."

"Don't you understand that it's God's will. You can't

prevent the girl from confronting her destiny. You can't oppose the law of karma, nobody can. Everything is governed by karma. Karma is life."

Gandhi continues:

"Always have the holy name of the Lord upon your lips and you will be relieved from worry."

"Lugdi Devi always had the holy name upon her lips," says Shanti Devi. "God's name was always with her. It was also with her when she reincarnated. I remember it."

"I understand," says Gandhi. "I hope to know more when you have been in Muttra. I'll be following you with loving thoughts. What is needed is more truth. Never step aside from the way of truthfulness, whatever it may cost."

"Bless us," says Prem Pyari. "We are so happy and proud."

"Good luck in Muttra. I'll leave all the details to Neki Ram Sharma and the other two gentlemen here. Tara Chad Mathur is a lawyer. He knows how everything should be done legally. One must follow all laws, great and small. But the most important law of all—love to all living beings—is in the heart."

Gandhi lifts up Shanti Devi and kisses her.

She puts her arms around his emaciated neck and cries against his shoulder.

The tiny, frail, toothless, yet powerful man strokes her hair tenderly.

"Can't you come with us to Muttra?" asks Shanti Devi. "You are so good, you are—like my Jeth."

Gandhi laughs and puts the girl down again.

The Journey to Muttra

November 24th, 1935, is a sunny and crisp chilly day. Fifteen highly respected people from Delhi are travelling on a train to Muttra together with the not-quite nine-year-old Shanti Devi.

The leadership for the Committee of enquiry has been assigned to the previously mentioned Tara Chand Mathur, Neki Ram Sharma and Lala Deshbandu Gupta.

Among the other members are noticeably another eminent lawyer, two newspapermen who are well-known all over India, a distinguished politician, some businessmen and government officials, all known for their impeccable character.

"The temple is going to be closed. We don't have time to get to the temple."

"What temple is it you are referring to?" asks Lala Deshbandu Gupta.

"The Dvarkadish temple. They close at twelve o'clock and don't open again until the evening. We won't be in time."

The hours go by and they approach Muttra. Everyone in the party observes Shanti Devi's reactions with great interest.

Now she wants to get nearer to the window.
"We're in Muttra!" she cries.

The meeting with Jeth

When the train arrives at the platform there are people everywhere.

Kedar Nath Chaubey and his family have been informed about the arrival of Shanti Devi and the Committee of enquiry.

Shanti Devi's group has only moved a few steps on the platform when she discovers someone she knows—an older man wearing widely-tailored, light-colored trousers.

Shanti Devi runs towards him and puts her arms around his legs and won't let go. She whispers something. He is taken by surprise and turns his face from the girl to the others who are approaching.

"It's incredible!" he exclaims. "Then it must be true." The whole group has gathered around the man and the girl. She must now tell them loudly and clearly who she has met. She has tears of happiness in her eyes.

It's my Jeth," she explains, "my brother-in-law."

The dignified brahmin is astonished and deeply touched.

"My name is babu Ram Chaubey," he says. "This child has asked me if I have looked after her holy basil plant which I had promised to do before she left us and travelled to Agra. It's true, Lugdi Devi told me before ... Lugdi Devi, then it really is you in this child's body? There is a brilliance in your eyes ..."

Tulsi is a holy plant which traditionally is used in connection with religious ceremonies.

Babu Ram Chaubey lifts up the girl and gives her a hug. She in turn, strokes his cheek. It's a deeply moving scene. The Committee received their first proof when they were just about to alight onto the platform.

Tara Chand Mathur presents the whole group to babu Ram Chaubaey. The girl stands beside him and hugs his hand as if she doesn't want to let it go.

"The purpose of our journey is to conduct an impartial investigation of the girl's statement about her previous life," says Tara Chand Mathur. "We would ask you not to speak to her before our assignment is finished."

"I understand," answers babu Ram Chaubey. "Be careful with the child. Lugdi Devi was so sensitive."

The yellow house

Babu Ram Chaubey departs with a bow. Neki Ram Sharma turns to Shanti Devi.

"We are now entrusting the leadership of this visit wholly on you, Shanti Devi. You must show us the way to the places you are familiar with and even decide what else we shall do. Can you guide us to the place where you have lived before?"

Shanti Devi looks around so that she can orientate herself. The group calls out after several taxicabs and the girl takes a seat in the first one.

During the ride she sits quietly for a while and Neki Ram Sharma thinks that she has lost her sense of locality, but she has not. She points towards a narrow street with several trees.

"Here," she says. "We can get off here and walk the rest of the way."

"Where are we making for?" asks Tara Chand Mathur.

"We are going to the first home I had when I was newly married," answers Shanti Devi. "My husband Kedar Nath bought the house for us. I shall never forget how happy I was. I was brought there by Kedar Nath on our wedding day, to my yellow house which I loved."

Tara Chaud Mathur and Neki Ram Sharma are listening, but without being astonished anymore. Everything is so objective, so believable. No comments are needed in spite of the fact that it is the most unusual experience they have ever witnessed.

Shanti Devi leads the way. The others follow her close at heel. Further away between the trees they catch a glimpse of an old man. He comes towards them with slow steps. Shanti Devi recognizes him immediately and runs towards him. She bends her head towards his knees and kisses his hands.

"It was you, babu Mahadev, who gave me my chureys, my ankle bracelets. Do you remember? You said: 'She shall dance in Krishna's honor, she is as agile as a gopi, one of those pure girls who love God.' You appreciateed my dancing."

"Blessed be the Lord," exclaims the brahmin. "Those were my own words. Then you have returned, Lugdi Devi. Blessed be the Lord."

"This is my father-in-law, Mahadev Chaubey, a very wise man," explains Shanti Devi proudly.

Everyone is listening devoutly. Now Shanti Devi takes command again.

"The house is a little bit further away. It is yellow." She is extremely excited. Neki Ram Sharma hurries after her.

"Yes, it is a house over there," he says, "but you must be mistaken. It's not yellow."

"Yes, it is yellow," says Shanti Devi obstinately. "I know it is."

She is silently disappointed. Everyone in the group can now see a decorative, medium-sized house which is completely painted in white.

"Never mind, it's easy to be mistaken on one point," says Tara Chand Mathur. "You have been right about so many other things."

"It is yellow," says Shanti persistently. "It must be yellow." She is extremely unhappy and is close to tears. "It's my house anyway."

She runs on ahead of the others into the garden where two men are standing talking to each other. They look in astonishment at the girl who doesn't take any notice of them. Then they discover the whole group which is hesitantly approaching. The main door is open and Shanti Devi goes straight in.

"I rent this house," says the older of the two men." I rent it from Kedar Nath Chaubey. This is a neighbor who also knows about the circumstances here. Lugdi Devi ... Yes, that was the name of Kedar Nath Chaubey's former wife. She's dead."

"This little girl, Shanti Devi, reckons she can prove that she is the reincarnation of Lugdi Devi, but she says that the house should be yellow."

The tenant nods his head in agreement.

"Yes, it was so. We had it repainted and paid for it ourselves. When Lugdi Devi was alive the house was yellow. That is absolutely correct."

A murmur is heard from the group of listeners. Yet another bit of proof can be added to the rest.

More evidence

Now Shanti Devi is standing in the doorway. She seems absolutely overjoyed.

"Hurry and come over here everyone. I will show you my room; I will show you everything."

Everyone goes into the house and Shanti Devi explains what changes have been made, even how the furniture was placed before.

"I will show you my room of worship on the top

floor," says Shanti Devi. "That's where I had my holy basil plant. My husband and I had our rooms on the top floor."

She jumps up the staircase and the others follow after. It's incredibly exciting to watch the changing expressions on her childish, yet mature face. She opens the door. When she can't find the altar she becomes disappointed. Then she says with a sigh of relief:

"No, it's true. It must naturally be gone. I took my plant with me to the second house we had and my corner of devotion is also there, but I lived here with my husband. Here is where my bed stood."

"That's correct,' confirms the tenant." We went through the house when we were about to rent it and we saw where Kedar Nath and his wife had their rooms. May I ask the girl a question which is almost a little too frank?"

Tara Chand Mathur and Neki Ram Sharma give their permission.

"Yes, then I would just like to know where the house's jai-zarur is placed."

Jai-zarur is a dialectical slang expression, a typical Muttra word which none of the guests from Delhi had heard before.

Shanti Devi becomes slightly embarrassed but then jumps down the stairs.

"Here," she cries and knocks on a door.

The tenant laughs and explains in a whisper for Tara Chand Mathur what sort of thing a jai-zarur is. The word means "by force" and is used by the inhabitants of Muttra instead of the word toilet. There is a general laugh when the connection is understood.

The group says goodbye to the tenant and his neighbor and they move on.

A home

The old street of the Chaubey's in Muttra bears witness to an unusual spectacle, a procession which is led by a serious little girl. Suddenly she spots a young man.

"It's my brother," she cries. "Nuthura Nath, my brother."

She grabs him by his neck. He can't be more than twenty-five years old. He opens his arms and hugs her, taken by surprise. He is slender and well-built.

"My brother and I were so alike," cries Shanti Devi. "You became angry when people thought you were like your sister, do you remember?"

The young man nods his head and smiles with pearly-white teeth.

"How do you know that? Is it you who is Lugdi Devi? May I ask if you know the names of your two other brothers?"

"Vitala Nath and Ayodhya Nath," laughs Shanti Devi. "Should I not know the names of my own brothers? I am very fond of all my relatives."

At this stage, everyone has become accustomed to Shanti Devi's outstanding memory.

Shanti Devi and her brother from her previous life begin a lively conversation. They ask each other questions as if it were a competition. Shanti Devi's answers are spontaneous and without hesitation. She is self-confident and happy.

"Something godlike inspires her," says Lala Deshbandu Gupta. "There is no question about that."

Shanti Devi now shows a changed attitude; she is more subdued. When she approaches the home where Kedar Nath and his family still live, her carriage becomes that of a grown woman.

Tàra Chand Mathur studies her and he fancies he can discern the contours of another being—a woman who has been on trial and matured.

Shanti Devi points to the house. There are no childish tones in her voice.

"It was here I spent the happiest time of my life, but also the most difficult. I was extremely ill."

Kedar Nath Chaubey, his wife and Lugdi Devi's son, Naunita Lal, are waiting in the hall. Shanti Devi curtsies reverently and hides her face somewhat with her sari.

She goes up to her son and kisses him on the forehead. She greets Kedar Nath's wife, who blushes and hides her face, with reserved curtsey. It's a strange scene. After that, Shanti Devi makes a gesture to allow the group to come nearer.

"You are all welcome," she says. "It was here I spent most of my time as a married woman when I was Lugdi Devi. Now I'll show you everything—my house, my holy basil plant, my clothes, my jewelry, everything. You understand, Kedar Nath, that we are here to verify that what I've said about my previous life is the truth. Nobody is allowed to speak to me. I will describe everything myself. We won't stay long."

The Brahmin seems much more upset than Shanti Devi.

"God be with you, Lugdi/Shanti Devi," he says. "You may stay as long as you wish and do as you please. After all, this was your home, Lugdi Devi."

"This was my real home," says the girl. "I lived here as a real woman. The kitchen is out there. We can have a look at it, if you like. Then we can go upstairs, where I shall show you my room. There is also the corner where I used to pray and my plant."

Kedar Nath wants to say something, but she is already a good bit up the stairs. He follows her and unlocks a door. Shanti Devi's expression turns to stone. It's quite obvious that the room isn't used anymore. There is only a large cupboard and several packing cases.

"Where is my holy basil plant?" she asks suddenly. "Babu Ram said that he has taken care of it. What have you done with my room? Where is my prayer corner."

Kedar Nath seems embarassed.

"Babu Ram still has your plant. There is nothing wrong with it. It's extremely large. Your room ... Yes, times change and ..."

"Where is Krishna's picture, Kedar Nath? Isn't it still here? I loved it."

"It is somewhere. I don't quite know where," says Kedar Nath rapidly. "Why should your room be the same way as it was before ... I'm so sorry, Lugdi Devi, I just didn't know better."

Lugdi Devi's jewelry

Shanti Devi goes into the room and stands before the large cupboard.

"You are not using it anyway for anything. I don't like that cupboard. My bed stood there before."

"Yes, that's correct," says Kedar Nath. "Her bed stood there."

Shanti Devi observes Kedar Nath and there is tenderness in her expression, no accusation. Even so, it's as if an ongoing settlement is taking place between this couple who now meet again.

"I had some clothes in this cupboard," says Shanti Devi. "It was standing on the groundfloor before. Are my clothes still here?"

Kedar Nath's wife is standing behind him. He gives her an irresolute glance. She shakes her head.

"No, of course not, they can't still be here after such

a long time," says Shanti Devi. "What about my jewelry—my chureys?"

"Yes, of course. They are still here," says Kedar Nath.

He appears with a jewelry box which he unlocks. Shanti Devi's childish hands delve into the jewelry. There are pearl necklaces, bracelets and ankle-bracelets. She picks up a splendid string of pearls with a ruby which she hangs over her forehead and fastens around her head.

"It's my chand," she says. "You gave it to me, Kedar Nath. Isn't it beautiful?"

She looks in the mirror, but when she sees her reflection, she flinches. She starts to look in the box again.

"That's mine—that's not mine. You gave me this ring when we were married. That ring ... Those rings are hers."

She turns toward Kedar Nath's wife who draws up her sari and begins to cry. She hurries out of the room. She can't stand it any longer.

"Forgive me," says Shanti Devi. "Did I upset her? It was not my intention."

"I know that," whispers Kedar Nath, "but one must not ask too much."

"I'm not asking for anything," says Shanti Devi. "Here ... here are my chureys (ankle bracelets) that Mahadev gave me."

A reflex of a cry of joy from the past makes her eyes sparkle. She puts the ankle bracelets around her ankles and dances a few steps. The gold and silver makes a jingling noise.

The next step she takes makes the ankle bracelets glide off. Her ankles are far too slender for a grown woman's jewelry.

"Would you like to have them?" entreats Kedar Nath. "Would you like to have them back?"

"No," she answers. "Let's go now."

They leave the room. Everyone is quiet. The atmosphere is melancholic after everything that has been witnessed.

"There is my white sari," says Shanti Devi in passing. "I recognize it."

She points to a table where a pile of laundry is lying. She laughs. It is no childish laugh.

"Is there something else you would like to know before we go to the temple?"

"We are convinced," says Tara Chand Mathur. "I am speaking on behalf of all of us when I say that we are convinced."

The forgotten well

"The well!" exclaims Neki Ram Sharma. "You have spoken so much about a well where you used to sit and polish your silver vessels. I ask, not because I don't believe you, but because I'm curious."

"I shall show you the well," answers Shanti Devi. They go out into the large courtyard. There is a cupboard with vessels of silver and other valuable items which would only be expected in such a well-to-do household. The floor is paved with stone. Shanti Devi looks around.

"The holy pictures are gone," she says.

"But where is the well?" asks Neki Ram Sharma." I can't see even the slightest trace of it."

"The well is over there," says Shanti Devi.

She points towards a corner of the courtyard, but nobody can discover any well there. One almost feels a certain relief that she could be wrong.

Kedar Nath goes to the appointed corner. He bends down and lifts several stones away.

"We have boarded-up the well," he says. "I myself

had almost forgotten about it. The water had become contaminated. One is unable to find the well if they don't know where it is. You can see that there is still a little water down there on the bottom."

The witnesses come nearer and establish the fact that there had been a well at the appointed place. Down at the bottom of the well the surface of the water glimmers.

The secret hiding place

"Let's go back, up to my room," says Shanti Devi. "I will show you where I had my money hidden, the money I was saving for my son."

She goes up the stairs and Kedar Nath opens the deserted room again. The witnesses wonder what she means, as within is not the slightest glimpse of a hiding place. Shanti Devi goes to a corner of the room and, using her foot, she tries to lift up a floorboard.

"Can you help me lift up the floorboard?"

Apparently the floorboard is quite loose. When Kedar Nath prys up the floorboard, a hiding place between the two floors is exposed. It is fairly deep. Shanti Devi thrusts her hand and forearm into the hole, right up to her shoulder.

"My money is gone. I know it was there. One hundred fifty rupees!"

All she manages to find are several pieces of rubble which she is holding in her hand.

"Where is my money, Kedar Nath?" she asks. The brahmin turns away and avoids her glance.

"I have spent it, I have spent it … Why should it still be here? It seemed pointless to let it just lie there."

"What did you do with it, Kedar Nath?"

"I paid for the funeral," he says in a hushed voice.

"You said earlier that you forgot to sacrifice it. You said that there was such a rush with the funeral. You said ..."

"Yes, I know. I broke my promise to Lugdi Devi. It still torments me terribly."

The mature man and the little girl who also shows a singular kind of maturity, look at each other in silence. The witnesses have a feeling that they are now touching upon something which extends over and above even such an investigation as this one.

Maybe we'll meet again

"We really should be content with the results of our investigation," says Neki Ram Sharma seriously. "I ask you in front of all these witnesses, pandit Kedar Nath Chaubey, what is your opinion about this little girl who has told us of her reminiscences of her preious life?"

"I recognize my dead wife, Lugdi Devi, in this child," answers Kedar Nath. "She was a wonderful person, faithful in all her duties."

Everyone is deeply moved. Shanti Devi casts a last glance at the home that once was hers.

"Goodbye, Kedar Nath," she says. "Maybe we'll meet again."

"You are always welcome here ... home," he answers.

A girl with two mothers

Surprisingly enough, Shanti Devi has not mentioned very much about her parents in her previous life. It would seem that her recollection of them is blurred by the presence of her parents in the present incarnation. When she spoke about her Real home, she always meant her home with Kedar Nath. When she was very small she spoke now and then about her Real parents, her Real mother. On several occasions she mentioned the name of her father, Chaturbhuj Chaubey. She had only mentioned once the name of her mother in her previous life.

Childhood home

On the way from Kedar Nath's house to the temple, she stops the taxicabs a short distance away from a white wall. She gets out on the street and the whole group follows after her—a good bit behind.

She stops and finds the entrance. Then she stands at

the door and looks in towards the large garden behind the wall.

"This is my childhood home," she says, "but there are so many people here!"

She steps into the garden without regard and the group follows slowly after. Evidently there is some kind of party going on. There are at least 50 people, mostly women.

This situation is perhaps even more trying for her than those earlier that day. This is about her origin and childhood in her previous incarnation.

"Are you ever satisfied?" sighs Prem Pyari in a whisper. "How much must a mother put up with? What's happening to my child?"

"Mama, Mama," cries Shanti Devi.

But it is not to Prem Pyari she turns. Shanti Devi rushes up to an impressive, middle-aged lady in an expensive sari, who turns out to be her aunt in her previous incarnation. Shanti Devi lifts up her arms towards her.

The lady looks confused. Then she gives the girl a hug. But something feels wrong.

"No, it's not you," says Shanti Devi. "You are not Jagti Devi, my mother."

Gasps of surprise are heard from the women. Then everybody quietens down.

Shanti Devi runs up to a fairly simply-dressed, prematurely-aged lady. She puts her arms around her and begins to cry. The old lady looks absolutely confused.

One child, two mothers

"Mama, Mama, Jagti Devi," shouts Shanti Devi. "It's Lugdi Devi, your daughter."

The old lady shakes her head as if she doesn't understand. Then Shanti Devi speaks in a whisper to her so that none of the others can hear. The old lady looks perplexed and draws the girl towards her. Shanti Devi must repeat what she has just said.

She is snivelling the whole time, and so does the old lady. Then they both cry together.

Prem Pyari has stayed at the gateway looking on as a spectator. Everyone, both the witnesses outside the wall and the guests within, can see the agony she's in. She puts both hands in front of her face to hide her tears.

"My God," she whispers, "now they are taking my little girl away from me. What shall I do?"

The scene is almost unbearable. Everyone is standing there feeling bewildered and helpless. Shanti Devi's tears are no ordinary tears. It's almost as if an inhuman burden has been lifted away. It's an incredible release, but at the same time extremely painful.

At that moment, Tara Chand Mathur, the lawyer steps into the garden. He feels that this gamble with fate should not be driven too far.

"I'm sorry," he says. "I'm responsible for all this and feel it's gone far enough. I can't permit it to continue."

He loosens the girl from Jagti Devi's arms and guides her gently towards Prem Pyari. Prem Pyari clings firmly to her daughter who tries to free herself.

Jagti Devi stretches out her arms after her child she has now lost a second time.

"She asked me if I had offered flowers and pastries to Krishna which I had promised her I would at the hospital in Agra," says Jagti Devi. "I forgot to do as she had asked me. Now she asked me to do this today. When I embraced her, it was Lugdi Devi I held in my arms. She was my little girl."

"You didn't do as I asked, mama," cries Shanti Devi.

"So now I must do it. Why has everyone broken their promises? Why does one always lie to a dying person?"

"This must surely be enough now," says Prem Pyari suddenly. "The girl is ours anyway. She is ill, her whole body is trembling."

"I am not ill," protests Shanti Devi. "Leave me alone. You are not my real mother. My real mother is Jagti Devi and there is my father, Chaturbhuj Chaubey."

She frees herself and runs towards an older man dressed in a typical Muttra costume. He had been standing beside the others and observing the trend of events.

"You ... You are Lugdi Devi, our girl," he murmurs. "Child ... You knew that I am Chaturbhuj Chaubey. Is there anything else you can tell me?"

Shanti Devi hesitates.

"You were very poor," she says candidly. "You had to put yourself in debt to be able to pay for my dowry because you wanted me to be the wife of the wealthy Kedar Nath Chaubey."

In some way the strained atmosphere is eased by this remark.

"It's true, he says. "I was very poor; poorer than I am now. The girl is right, but why haven't you told us that she would be coming to see us? How long may our recovered daughter stay with us?"

Prem Pyari and Rang Bahadur walk towards the Brahmin and try and get the girl to go with them.

"She cannot be your daughter," says Rang Bahadur. "We have brought her up, she is still ours."

"But please, let her stay awhile," asks Jagti Devi humbly. "We loved our Lugdi Devi so much. We promise to make her happy. Would she not like to live in Lugdi Devi's home, play with her toys, wear her clothes? We have saved everything because we loved her so much."

"It's impossible," says Rang Bahadur. "Isn't that going against nature, against us? I suspected this would happen. I have warned you, but nobody has listened to me."

"They want to steal the girl from us," says Prem Pyari. "Everyone is taking part in this conspiracy."

"Let the girl choose," says Jagti Devi. "She is the only one who has the right to choose. None of us has that right."

Prem Pyari looks pleadingly at Tara Chand Mathur but he only nods his head consentingly. Her husband stands there, motionless, without changing his expression.

"It's fate, my dear wife," he says. "It's karma. We are all slaves under the law of karma."

Shanti Devi stands there hesitantly and contemplates. It's a difficult decision for her to make. She's not crying any longer, but is deeply serious.

At last she surrenders herself to Rang Bahadur and Prem Pyari. When she walks out through the door, she turns back and whispers:

"Forgive me, mother Jagti. Forgive me, father Chaturbhuj."

In the temple

The news about Shanti Devi and her visit to Muttra has spread like wildfire. The inhabitants of Muttra are on their feet. People are coming from all directions. They are following after the taxicabs. Everyone wants to get as near as possible to her. The air is vibrating with questions and shouting.

When Shanti Devi turns around, she notices how crowded the streets are with people who have attentively followed her every move.

She is used to crowds from Delhi, so she is not disturbed by it. The crowds increase. The taxicabs have difficulty getting through. It's like a triumphal procession and it's possible that Shanti Devi regards it as such.

She smiles and looks around in all directions. Her childish face is radiating irresistibly. People cheer joyously.

"Lugdi Devi, you've come back to us!"

She stands up in the carriage and greets the onlookers with her hands clasped to her breast and with her head bent forward. The crowds are cheering and shouting.

They are approaching Dvarkaish temple. The enormous bronze-door has just opened. The girl runs up the stairs. Priests in orange-colored attire observe her. Perhaps they are surprised over her enthusiasm.

Shanti Devi falls on her knees in the doorway and bows her head towards the floor. The group is approaching slowly behind her. The whole of the temple-courtyard is packed with people.

"Oh, Dvarkaish Hari," the girl cries. "Oh, Dvarkadish, receive me. I am Lugdi Devi who has reincarnated."

In the darkness of the temple, the beautiful dancing figure of Krishna in gold and silver starts to move. He really is dancing. It is not an illusion. The Dvarkaish Hari's picture is a technical masterpiece.

The girl creeps nearer on her bare feet until she stands before him and can look him in the eyes.

"Krishna, Krishna," whispers Shanti Devi. "Help me as you have always done."

Shanti Devi speaks to the people

Afterwards Shanti Devi descends the Vishrant Ghat toward Jumna, the holy river. The crowd stands aside when she approaches. The shouts of joy have quieted and are followed by a solemn atmosphere.

The people are standing still and watch the child move with dignity down towards the river. They see her shrouded in flowers by the priests.

Down by the river, Shanti Devi takes off the garlands of flowers and lays them carefully on the surface of the water. She drinks some water and wants to bathe in the river.

But Tara Chand Mathur stops her.

"Dear child, we don't have time for that. The people have asked us to assemble in a public place and give them an account of what has happened. Will you let them meet you? Would you like to say something yourself?"

"Yes," answers Shanti Devi.

They now leave the river. The taxicabs drive them to a schoolyard nearby, where an improvised tribunal is quickly arranged. It's a large schoolyard. Thousands of people have gathered and there is still a continuous flow of people making an appearance.

Tara Chand Mathur and Neki Ram Sharma give a detailed report of what has happened and the other members of the Committee confirm what has been said.

At last, even Shanti Devi makes a speech. She is dignified and serious. She ends her short speech by saying:

"I'm happy I've lived here, but now I intend to continue my new life in Delhi."

It's now late in the evening. Shanti Devi is extremely tired from all the excitement and new experiences. Tara Chand Mathur is obliged to dismiss a group of local villagers who want them to remain there at least until the next day.

On the train home, Shanti Devi says a few words before falling asleep:

"When I'm grown up I'll move to Muttra."

The Committee of Inquiry photographed in Mathura (Muttra) on November 24, 1935. Shanti Devi is sitting on her father's lap. Lawyer Tara Chand Mathur is standing in the uppermost row, fifth from the right.

The Committee was convinced that Shanti Devi,s story on all accounts, was credible and true.

A fully proven case of reincarnation was the Committee's verdict.

My first meeting with Shanti Devi

When the Committee of enquiry came back to Delhi a report was written describing the experiences witnessed during the visit to Muttra.

Everyone was in agreement that Shanti Devi's reactions had been genuine through and through and that Lugdi Devi/Shanti Devi is irrefutably a case of genuine reincarnation. The report was published. The material was also presented to several noted scientists for analysis. Nobody was able to deny the evidence which was put forward.

Shanti Devi continued with her schooling.

Now and then articles were written about her in newspapers, but that happened more and more rarely. Shanti Devi grew up to be a quiet and reserved woman.

She often thought about Kedar Nath. Sometimes she would receive a letter from him. There were infrequent but cordial messages exchanged between them. She came to regard Kedar Nath as an extraordinary relative.

When World War II broke out Rang Bahadur's economy deteriorated. Imminent ruin stood at the door.

Shanti Devi finished school and offered to get a job to help the family's economy. She was 15 years old at the time.

Her parents had a heartfelt and sincere wish that Shanti Devi should be married to the wealthy Devendra Tayal. He had declared that he was willing to pay for her education at the University in Simla.

But Shanti Devi refused.

In her heart Shanti Devi experienced that she had a split personality. Kedar Nath had remarried and Lugdi Devi was dead—officially dead.

She could never have Kedar Nath back again, although she still felt attached to him. When she became sad and disconsolate, the past caught up with her with a terrible force. It was as if it wanted to destroy the personality of Shanti Devi that it had cost her such great efforts to maintain.

To her parent's dismay she declared that she had decided she would never marry.

"I am a widow," she declared, "and in accordance with the unwritten laws, a widow is not allowed to marry again. I still love my husband. I hold his memory sacred and nobody else can take his place. Nobody can alter my decision."

A proposal

In spite of the family's poor financial situation, Shanti Devi was sent to the University in Simla, a town in the north on the flatland below the foot of the Himalaya Mountains.

For Shanti Devi it was an immense step forward to be able to study. The subjects were English, Hindi and

Sanskrit. She was well aware of the sacrifice it meant for her parents. She lived in seclusion, studied diligently and often felt terribly lonely.

After a while she became acquainted with a young sikh whose name was Ramdas Singh. They had mutual interests.

The almost 20-year-old Shanti Devi felt a warm interest for the young man, but inwardly she had the continual feeling that she couldn't betray Kedar Nath.

In the end, when Ramdas Singh proposed to her, she told him everything about her previous life and about her experiences as Lugdi Devi.

Even though he urgently asked her to forget all about it and live in the present, she declared that she didn't feel free to marry him.

They separated.

When Shanti Devi graduated she returned to Delhi. She seemed calm and happy and didn't speak of Kedar Nath or Muttra anymore. Her parents hoped her common sense would guide her towards getting married.

Rang Bahadur had accepted a position with Devendra Tayal, whose firm, a paper factory, flourished. Shanti Devi's two sisters were already married and the family's future seemed promising.

As it was her father's wish, Shanti Devi started to work for Devendra Tayal, but as far as marriage was concerned, she wouldn't hear of it.

The picture of Kedar Nath was as alive as ever in her mind's eye, but she never spoke to anyone about her past and Devendra Tayal didn't embarrass her either with any advances or bear pressure upon her.

What Shanti Devi's hopes were for the future, nobody knew.

In the year 1947 she received a message notifyng her

that Ramdas Singh had been killed in combat between the Muslims and Hindus, a conflict which had been kindling ever since India had won her freedom.

What shall I do with my life?

During this time Shanti Devi had contact with Narsingh Guru Maha, who was a priest in the temple at Mandaleshvar outside Delhi. She became his yoga student. She also came to know Sushil Chandra Bose, a learned man who was especially interested in the time in between her lives as Lugdi Devi and Shanti Devi.

"This period is shrouded in darkness," says Shanti Devi. "I experience a strong resistance about telling you what I remember. If there is really something which should be forbidden to talk about, it ought to be this." However his questions awakened both diffuse and distinct memories within her. She didn't see herself as the living Lugdi Devi, but as the dead Lugdi Devi. A new perspective opened up out of the darkness which had earlier always been so painful.

At night her parents were often awakened by her crying. In dreams she continually experienced her own death. She looked pale and worn out during this time. Her parents were worried about her health, not without reason.

Another person with whom she had renewed contact during this time was Maitri Deviji, the Holy Mother. Shanti Devi studied philosophy under her supervision. She could speak openly to her about her problems and the perpetual question: what shall I do with my life?

I visit Tara Chand Mathur

She soon terminated her office job at the paper factory to be able to wholly devote herself to teaching. Her dream was to be able to build her own school. Together with her parents and her brother she bought a piece of land outside of Delhi for this purpose.

It was at about this time I heard about the reincarnated Indian girl, Shanti Devi. I had for a long time been particularly interested in India and had studied Indian culture for several years.

I had a discussion about Shanti Devi with a well-known Indian who lived in Stockholm at the time, professor Shyam Sundar Goswami. He referred to quite a number of other cases but he said that it was impossible to prove anything.

I searched in libraries but could not find any information about Shanti Devi. The Indian Embassy stated they believed that a noted lawyer in Delhi, Tara Chand Mathur, had been involved in the matter.

After some time I travelled to England where I, among others, spoke to an Indian yogi who had some information to give me.

Eventually I had collected enough material to enable me to travel to India.

As soon as I had arrived in Delhi I contacted the lawyer, Tara Chand Mathur.

He seemed extremely able to inspire confidence. He had a position in the High Court and was a highly respected Indian citizen.

He told me that the members who took part in the Committee of investigation had split up but that he could give me all the facts.

One thing I immediately asked was whether he was

During the preliminary inquiries which I had made in Sweden and England, I came to the conclusion that an eminent lawyer in Delhi, Tara Chand Mathur, had been one of the leaders in the Committee of inquiry which had established the genuineness of the reincarnation case of Lugdi Devi/Shanti Devi.

The first thing I did therefore, when I came to Delhi was to look up Tara Chand Mathur. We had a long conversation in his office.

convinced that the girl could not possibly have been exposed to any sort of hypnotic influence.

The lawyer smiled faintly where he sat at his desk.

"That is something we can leave out of the discussion entirely," he said. "The girl was only four years old when she started to say things which didn't have anything to do with her ordinary surroundings. She was entirely under her parents' supervision. Nobody would have had any opportunity to hypnotize her."

Before leaving the lawyer's office I was given all the documents relevant to the case of Shanti Devi. The more I read, the more convinced I became that the occurrence which took place in Delhi and Mathura, and which is related in this book, is one of the most extraordinary events that has happened on Earth in modern times.

Episode after episode, a general picture emerges. All Shanti Devi's statements and actions can be explained psychologically. There are no contradictions.

Nobody can be so naïve as to believe that there could have been a possibility of a conspiracy between Shanti Devi, her parents, some of Delhi's most respected citizens and lastly but not least, the Indian leader, Mahatma Gandhi himself.

What would be the purpose of such a conspiracy?

Shanti Devi has neither gained wealth or fame from it, nor has anyone else.

It's quite probable that she could have lived, if not in luxury, at least as a central figure in a new religious sect if she had wanted to, but this has not happened.

Few people in the west had actually heard about Shanti Devi at the time. It was almost by chance I managed to track her down.

Early the following day I went together with Tara Chand Mathur's two sons to Shanti Devi's home. The young men had, as we have seen, known Shanti Devi ever since she was small.

I meet Shanti Devi

I am taken into a room where I am presented to Shanti Devi's parents.

Her father is pale skinned and aristocratic. He speaks excellent English while his wife can only speak a few words. She seems older than her husband, has darker skin and is more reserved.

We begin to speak about Shanti Devi. I ask them if there could have been a possibility that someone in the family or someone they are acquainted with could have told her about Muttra when she was small, or perhaps some person she had met outside on the street?

"Absolutely not," says Rang Bahadur, emphatically. "We never leave the children unattended here in India. To the best of our knowledge she never had any contact with anyone from Muttra until she was presented to Kedar Nath and those he brought with him.

"She was almost mute until she was four years old," he continues. "Then she spontaneously began to talk about her past life. We tried to ignore her. What can one do to convince a four year old that her parents are not her parents; that her home is not her home; that she lives in an strange town which she has never heard about? How does one get her to speak a dialect which one doesn't understand? How does one convince a four year old that she is married and has a son? It's impossible to carry out such deceit."

Shanti Devi's brother, Viresh Narain, who works for the Indian airlines comes home, and soon even Shanti Devi herself is standing by the door. She gives one the impression of being ordinary, charming and girlish even though she is a mature woman.

During the conversation which follows, Shanti Devi talks about her two lives. Calmly and objectively.

"I remember that which happened in my past life. I remember my childhood in Delhi and I remember my childhood in Muttra. The first part of my childhood in Delhi was the most difficult because I didn't quite understand that I was a child and that I lived in Delhi. I believed that I was in Muttra, and I had to be continually reminded that I was in Delhi. Eventually I understood. I had to learn that I was a child and not a grown woman. I learned that I had other parents and that I must accept my new surroundings. As the years went by it became easier. It was a period of adjustment, however, the whole time I had double recollections of everything."

"Were your recollections defined and ready from the beginning?"

"It always seems that one remembers one thing after the other. One hesitates—was it really like that?— and suddenly one has a clear picture. Then one has new associations, one remembers more and more. Sometimes one is absolutely certain from the beginning, sometimes not, until later on."

"Do you still recall new details?"

"It happens occasionally."

"Do you have to make an effort to recall your recollections—to force yourself?"

"I didn't know what it meant to remember, when I was very small. It was so alive. I didn't reflect over the actual procedure. My earlier life was still with me. It had never really come to an end. It was my Real life, the other was like a dream. My past life as Lugdi Devi was so intense. When it didn't correspond with the reality around me it

Sitting from the left: Shanti Devi's father, Rang Bahadur, Shanti Devi and Prem Pyari, Shanti Devi,s mother.
Standing: Viresh Narian, Shanti devi's brother.
Photo: Sture Lönnerstrand.

became a torment. Just imagine a small child in this situation. I didn't understand how the whole thing was connected. Now and then it was most confusing, but then it became clearer and clearer."

"Now you don't have any difficulty differentiating between your earlier life and your present life?"

"No, now I know that I don't have two personalities within me, but that there are two different periods."

We sit quietly. Eventually I ask: "Do you also remember the period after your death? The time which passed in between Lugdi Devi's death in Agra and Shanti Devi's birth in Delhi? It was over a year if I'm not mistaken."

"It was exactly one year, two months and seven days," Shanti Devi says. "Yes. I remember that period as well, if one can call it remembering."

"What do you mean?"

"It's something which can't quite be explained in words. One can remember things which manifest in life, but when it concerns death it's different."

"Your experiences were not based upon sensations in the normal meaning?"

"No, they ceased when I died, but one doesn't die as quickly as people usually believe."

"Now I don't understand. Isn't a person truly dead when they've been declared physically dead by a doctor?"

"No! However, I don't want to talk about that period. It's not right."

Before departing I ask her if she would like to accompany me to Muttra so that we both can experience something of her previous life, meet Kedar Nath, Lugdi Devi's son, Naunita Lal, as well as her parents in her previous incarnation.

"My parents are dead," she says. "The last time I was in Muttra I decided I would never visit it again. I have left a life behind me there, a life which I have lost, but if you wish I will accompany you."

The meeting with Kedar Nath

Mathura, the Indian equivalent of Bethlehem, is about 150 to 200 kilometers south of Delhi and is an important place of pilgrimage.

The train slowly draws in towards Muttra's Railway station. We are in the Holy city, Krishna's city, Shanti Devi Mathur's Mathura.

Shanti Devi is back in the Real city, on the well-known streets. She sees the silhouettes of the temples. It is the Muttra of dreams. The holy gates of the clocktower raise their well-known landmark now as in the past.

When we come to Mathura the first thing we do is to visit Kedar Nath Chaubey's store. There we are welcomed by Naunita Lal, Lugdi Devi's son.

He is a well-built young man with a neatly trimmed mustache who politely welcomes his mother. He invites us to come in and he presents his son for us, Shanti Devi's "grandchild". Shanti Devi speaks unaffectedly and naturally with her son, precisely as if she had been his real mother.

Perhaps Naunita Lal is somewhat less respectful towards her than he ought to be according to the Indian concept. After all, they are both the same age. Whatever feelings they may have for each other deep inside, they certainly don't show them.

Then an old man comes up to them who is wearing a brown costume. It is Shanti Devi's Jeth, Kedar Nath's older brother.

When he leaves us after a while Kedar Nath himself

Shanti Devi visits her husband from her previous life, Kedar Nath (to the right in the picture) in his store in Muttra.

To the left, Naunita Lal, Lugdi Devi's son.

In the middle, Shanti Devi's "grandchild."

Photo: Sture Lönnerstrand.

appears, a dignified Brahmin dressed in black. Considering he's around 60 years old, he looks surprisingly youthful.

"This is my husband from my previous life," says Shanti Devi."

Her pride is obvious. She regards Kedar Nath Chaubey with shining eyes. Neither can one mistake the radiance in Kedar Nath's.

I have a peculiar feeling that neither of them perceive each other fully realistically.

In Shanti Devi's eyes Kedar Nath is still a young man, and for Kedar Nath Shanti Devi is still his beloved deceased wife. Two people who meet again after a long separation. They speak with each other in hushed voices in Hindi.

"You aren't often here, Shanti Devi," he says. "You haven't answered my letters."

He laughs somewhat embarrassed and observes Shanti Devi who feels tears come to her eyes when he looks at her.

"No, please don't cry again," he says. "We have both cried enough. Our karma is heavy enough to bear. Shanti Devi, would you not like to go home with me, home to the house that Lugdi and I shared?"

Shanti Devi nods her head in approval.

The house is painted in white and has some ornamental plaiting hung over the windows and doors. The interior is rather run-down. We drink strong spiced tea and Kedar Nath tells us what has happened since they last met.

Afterwards he shows us the house. Kedar Nath introduces us to his wife, a lady in a flame red colored sari. We are also introduced to his daughter-in-law, Naunita Lal's wife. She looks as if she would rather escape from

Shanti Devi shows the author the well that was one of the most crucial pieces of evidence.

everything.

She regards Shanti Devi as her mother-in-law and it's just not fitting to sit beside her mother-in-law, explains Kedar Nath.

Lastly, we go through a narrow corridor and come out into the much discussed courtyard where Lugdi Devi used to sit and polish the silver while she was waiting for her husband to arrive home.

I'm also allowed to see the well which was closed down and which was one of the most crucial pieces of evidence proving that the Lugdi/Shanti Devi story is true.

He has become old

When we are about to leave Muttra we are accompanied to the station by Kedar Nath, Naunita Lal and some other relatives from Shanti Devi's past.

The train is delayed and we sit for quite a while in the waiting room.

Kedar Nath and Shanti Devi don't make any secret of the fact that they are deeply affected by their meeting with each other. Kedar Nath is deeply moved. His eyes are filled with tears. His hand seeks Shanti Devi"s.

"Who knows if we'll meet again," says Kedar Nath with a sigh. "Time goes so quickly and I'm beginning to get old. It's a tragedy that we can never have our happiness back again."

"Would you perhaps like Shanti Devi to stay with you?" I ask. "Is that your secret wish?"

"I don't have the right to express such a wish," says Kedar Nath. "I am married to another woman. Shanti Devi is young and unmarried. I was unfaithful to Lugdi Devi and I broke my oath. I felt at the time that I had

The adults in the photograph are from left to right: "Jeth", Kedar Naths older brother, Naunita Lal and Kadar Nath.
Photo: Sture Lönnerstrand.

acted sensibly. However, I have pondered over it a great deal and I now realize that I acted foolishly. Everything would have been different if only I hadn't broken my promise."

"He broke the promise he gave me on my deathbed," says Shanti Devi. "He promised me then that he would never remarry. He gave me his promise under oath. He did it voluntarily. I didn't demand it of him."

"When I broke my promise, I thought that I am a man in the best years of my life," says Kedar Nath. "How could I possibly know that Lugdi Devi would come back again? She promised me of course. ..."

"What did she promise you?"

"She promised that we would see each other again. She promised me in the name of Krishna. How could I possibly know that such things really can happen? I have regretted it deeply, but what can I do. I have asked her to forgive me and I ask her once again."

"I forgive you," says Shanti Devi.

Their relationship really is one of the strangest imaginable. Two people who are so near to each other and yet at the same time so far away from each other, so bound by love and mutual reminiscences and yet so separated by different worlds and the passing of time.

"I felt the warmest and most ardent love for Lugdi Devi. She was as beautiful and affectionate as she was good and kind. Few men have had a woman with as many good qualities as she had. She fulfilled my wishes before I'd even had time to utter them. Lugdi Devi was deeply religious and in that respect she was far more advanced than myself. She had read the holy books and she practiced yoga. I missed her enormously when she left me."

Kedar Nath sighs and nobody can mistake the sincerity of his words.

It is quite true that it is not good for us to remember our earlier incarnations. What agony, what conflicts we are spared because we are protected by oblivion's merciful and reconciliating veil.

Shanti Devi has had to pay a high price. So has Kedar Nath and others close to her.

Shanti Devi waves to Kedar Nath who is still standing on the platform, alone and downhearted. When he turns to go he looks bent and tired. Shanti Devi gazes after him.

"He has become old," she whispers.

Her tears run slowly down her cheeks when she stands by the window and sees Muttra disappear in the evening haze.

I had to come back to Earth

During the following weeks, Shanti Devi and I meet every day. She also lets me meet her two philosophy teachers, Narsingh Guru Maha and Maitri Deviji.

"You are so experienced, you have been through so much. Do you teach?" I wonder.

"I have always wanted to be a teacher, but I have not advanced to that level yet," answers Shanti Devi. "However, I now have the keys to several well-kept secrets. Maitri Deviji's path is bhakti yoga, prayer and sincere devotedness. It was Lugdi Devi's way and it is mine as well. Lugdi Devi learned this great secret from the Master Yogiraja. It was he who guided her through the experience of death."

"What did she do?" I ask. "Or rather, how did she do it?"

"I don't know if I can tell you that," answers Shanti Devi. "I must ask the Holy Mother first. If she says that I may tell you, then I will do so. It is the greatest of all secrets. That which redeems us when we die."

"I would like us to travel together to the town where you died as Lugdi Devi," I tell her. "I would like to see Lady Lyall's hospital."

Shanti Devi gives a melancholy smile.

"I was not dead when my body made its last journey from Agra to Muttra. I died in Muttra just before my body was cremated and the ashes were scattered upon the Holy River. I simply can't talk about it. The thought makes me so depressed."

"You must," I persist. "In the Christian part of the world some people believe in spirits and ghosts. Others believe that the human body decays and crumbles to dust and later, after millions of years, is awakened to life on the last day of judgment. Many believe that there is no form of life or consciousness after death. They believe that death is the final, irrevocable obliteration of all life. Some people believe in heaven, some in the land of the dead, and others in hell. Many would rather not think about it at all. Make the most of the only life you have, they say, and push on to make as much money as you can and get as much as possible accomplished in life. They don't dare think too much about such matters."

"Heaven is within us," says Shanti Devi. "When a person develops, she also aquires greater knowledge, a better understanding of the Divine. Krishna is the Divine aspect which I embrace. He is the Savior who can be reached through prayer and faith."

"You ought to travel abroad and allow people to meet you," I say. " Why not get married and have children and a family?"

"Don't you understand that I can't do that? I can't get married while Kedar Nath is still alive. If he couldn't keep the promise he gave me on my deathbead, that's one thing. I don't blame him; but I've made my decision."

"Perhaps you'll meet someone. Love changes everything. It transforms things. Perhaps it would liberate you from the burden of the past?"

"I haven't met anyone," answers Shanti Devi. "I believe it's better to love all rather than one particular person."

The goal of man

The following morning we travel to Agra, which is not far away from Mathura. Shanti Devi's father and brother accompany us.

It was in Agra that Lugdi Devi experienced the conclusion of her earthly life. It was also here that the period between both incarnations began. What we are now interested in knowing about are her memories from the period in the out-of-body state between Lugdi Devi's and Shanti Devi's incarnations.

Agra is a relatively modern city. The foremost monument which represents past grandeur is the *Taj Mahal*, built in white marble. It is usually called the world's eighth wonder. The Taj Mahal was built in the 17th century by the Shah Jahan as a memorial to his beloved wife Mumtaz Mahal.

What can one say about this white dream in marble that hasn't already been said? It is the only truly magnificent building I have ever seen which is as blandishing and as strikingly beautiful as its equivalent pictured in the tourist brochures. Nobody can possibly be disappointed by the Taj Mahal.

In the atmosphere, in the sunny quietness, still lives the memory of a great love beyond words. How he must have loved his Mumtaz Mahal!

Lady Lyall's hospital is a large grey-white building. Shanti Devi points upwards towards a window.

"I was in the room up there." That's where I gave birth to my son; where I also died. I remember that I was extremely weak. Most of the time I was in a trance. One day I heard a nurse say: 'You have given birth to a son, Lugdi Devi!' How happy I was, but I knew at the same time that I had to die. I felt it in my whole body—though I fought against it with all the strength I had left. Naunita Lal was born on September 25, 1925."

"It was quite natural that you didn't want to die as young as you were."

"I prayed to Krishna without cessation in the way I had been taught. It was not a normal prayer. It was a mantra which leads a person through the state of death when she has lost her body. How I wanted to live and stay where I was on Earth at the same time! I made a great mistake. If I hadn't longed so desperately to come back, I would not have needed to incarnate again, but would have been reunited with Brahma and had eternal life."

Lugdi Devi was born on the January 18, 1902 and died at the hospital in Agra on the 4th of October, 1925, at 10 o'clock in the morning. She was 23 years old.

A while later, at the Taj Mahal, Shanti Devi continues to talk about Lugdi Devi's death.

"The goal of mankind is not to have more incarnations," she says. "It is instead to be liberated from the force of the Earth, to avoid new incarnations. When one has lived hundreds of lives, or perhaps thousands, then one should be mature enough to finally and permanently be reunited with the Divine.

"There are several ways by which the goal can be attained—to be liberated from reincarnation. One of them is the mantra method. Mantra is a type of prayer, but not in the Western sense. One continuously repeats God's name in a special way, until it fills the whole of one's consciousness, all of one's thoughts.

"I practiced repeating the holy name, Krishna's name, first several hours every day, then more and more until I repeated it day and night, every minute without a break. Eventually the mantra came into full effect. It was with me all the time. The prayer grew and grew, I didn't even need to think about it anymore. Then a great change took place."

"What happened?"

"I was transformed, I became incredibly happy. I wasn't able to think immorally and egotisticaly even if I wanted to. I was filled with a sense of spiritual strength and belief. Krishna became part of my being. I lived only for him; I breathed his name; my pulse sang his name. Krishna was in my heart, literally. I was strong and happy. I didn't listen to anything base."

We die gradually

"I lay there in Lady Lyall's hospital and repeated Krishna's name. I knew that I must die, yet I clung on to life. When a person clings to life desperately in that way, life clings to him or her. Five days before my death my teacher appeared. He advised me to prepare myself for death. From that moment nobody was allowed to meet me again, not even my mother,or even Kedar Nath. I wanted to be alone. There was no pain that could prevent me from repeating Krishna's name."

"But when you lost consciousness, could you continue to repeat the holy name?"

"Yes, I could, because it filled up the whole of my unconscious mind, because it had become a part of myself. At the same time it relieved me from all anxiety."

"We don't die suddenly but gradually," says Shanti Devi. "The body's different energy centers (chakras) cease to function in a certain order. Death starts from the bottom. The cold creeps slowly upwards. The heart has to work much harder until it's the only thing that seems to be alive. Then the breathing stops. But even when the heart has ceased to function, there is still life left in the brain, in the center which is called the third eye. Here there is a higher sensory organ which makes it possible for one to be able to see without eyes and hear without ears. Consciousness remains here for quite a while."

"For how long?"

"That depends on how intensely one has clung to the earthly life. It's quite possible that the one who has died is not even aware that he has died. Then it's a terrible shock for him when he realizes that he is without his body! However, there is nothing he can do about it. Liberation comes only when the life energy leaves the body and flows out into the power centers which are on the outside of and around the head. Something which we only have a vague idea about here on Earth.

"It gradually became dark. I felt the cold creep up all over me. I thought: Now I'm dead. I felt incredibly tired and couldn't move. I wanted to call out, but I couldn't. I wasn't in any pain. My heart had stopped beating, yet there was still some motion of my blood; a certain rhythm. Slowly, very slowly I began to hear Krishna's name as if through the surge from a waterfall. It was I, myself who continued to pronounce his name even after death. This is what I call the first part of death."

I remember my funeral

"Did the doctors come in and certify that you were dead?"

"Yes, a doctor and a nurse, my husband and my mother. Everyone was heartbroken. My husband embraced my body and wanted to kiss my mouth but the doctor restrained him. It was decided that they would immediately have my body taken away and have it conveyed to Muttra, where it was to be burned and the ashes strewn upon the river."

"Were you aware of what was happening the whole time? Did you see yourself and the others?"

"I was conscious, but I couldn't see in the usual way. I just knew. My life and consciousness were now contained within the ajna-chakra (the third eye). The third eye cannot be seen on an x-ray picture, but there is a gland there. Life is withdrawn there. India's holy men have since ancient times, understood how the soul enters into the body and even how it departs from the body, via the so-called secret ducts. Neither can the departure exit be discovered with the help of an x-ray but it coincides with an organ on the crown of the head."

"It is called the pineal gland. It is in this particular organ that Descartes believed that the soul resides," I remark.

"The lifeforce or energy, the Atman, remains there until it is set free," says Shanti Devi. "The word soul is far too vague. The Atman leaves the heart and continues to the third eye and lastly it arrives up on the crown of the head where it leaves the body forever. As long as the Atman is still confined to the third eye one senses what is happening. Although I was still inside my body I could in some strange way perceive it from the outside. Although I had no idea of time or space.

"Then I was back in Muttra, in the house where I had lived. Then I was taken down to the waterside. It was there I left my body forever before it was burned. Yet I was in some way aware of what was happening.

"My body was wrapped in silk and linen and was carried on a bier made of bamboo cane poles. It was covered with flowers. Kedar Nath lit the wood for the fire with the help of a holy vessel. The Priest gave his blessing and my relatives strolled around the funeral pyre with their faces turned the other way. I was no longer aware of what was happening. I had no other perceptions, other than that of an infinite bright light …

"This was the second death. I had arrived at a new stage. I had been led into another state of awareness. There was neither darkness nor light, neither day nor night, neither space nor time. It was just a new state of awareness."

The whole universe was within me

"Didn't you have any recollections of your body any longer?"

"No, I was free and I had shrunk. I was so tiny, almost like a minute particle of dust, like a feather, almost nonexistant. It was as if I was a germ which drifted around, here and there. Yet everything had room within me. Everything was within me. The whole universe was inside me.

"However, something was in constant motion, like a wind. It was a silver-grey stream of light which inclined back and forth. It was dead yet alive at the same time. It was a rhythm, as if someone was breathing, and I continued to repeat Krishna's name. All my incarnations were contained within this tiny germ.

"There were so many people around me there who were waiting to be purged from their sins and I was one of them. They represented all religions and all races. There was no difference between us."

"Was this the place which is usually called the land of the dead?"

"It wasn't a place. Everything was within me. My longing, my belief, my love, my horror; it was all on different levels inside me. I wanted to progress upwards, to improve, ascend higher ... I was given help. I saw Krishna as I had seen him earlier, as wonderful, and as forgiving ... No, even greater, even more forgiving."

"Did you recognize anyone there? Someone who had died?"

"There were so many faces, so many beings. I felt I knew them."

"Did you have a sense that you were out in space?"

"There was no sun, no moon, no Earth. Just this mild silver gleam of light which was in constant motion comparable to a faint gasp. Light beings disappeared and new ones appeared. We were all connected with each other. We were linked together with some sort of connecting radiating beams. We were as one. If we only realized how closely we are connected, we would never be able to hurt each other. We are all relatives through karma. Our destiny is interwoven through karma. It's only after death that we can truly realize the connection which we were unable to grasp or which we neglected throughout our lives. When someone does something good, everyone benefits by it. However, if someone does something terrible everyone suffers. It's not always noticeable immediately, but sooner or later it catches up with us.

"There are highly advanced and lower beings or whatever one can call them. They are on different levels, but it seemed to me that everything radiated from a mutual center, stationary and unchanging. There was a central sun, which I couldn't see, but only sense in some way."

"Did you have any idea how long you were in this state of awareness?"

"Neither time or space existed. I seemed to be floating until I found I was clinging on to something, wedged in between something. It was actually in the womb, but I couldn't understand it then. I had no thoughts, no words, no wordly concept to compare it with. I had been condemned to reincarnate. I was still not sufficiently spiritually developed to be reunited with God, Brahma. I had to come back to Earth in order to gain new experiences."

"I was not empty enough," says Shanti Devi.

"Empty?"

"Yes, I had so many desires and yearnings; I was so heavy that I couldn't elevate myself. I wanted to come back to Earth."

"You remembered your existence as Lugdi Devi?"

"All my memories returned in a concentrated form. I had a tremendous yearning to be a woman again, to be a person, a mother and wife."

"However, it was in vain. You could never again be Kedar Nath's wife."

"I didn't know that then."

"Can you explain why you, just you, of all people could remember your earlier incarnation and your existence in between your reincarnations?"

"I don't know," answers Shanti Devi. "Perhaps because I was able to repeat Krishna's name for such a long time. It's the only explanation I can give you. I was almost … I had almost reached a state of eternal bliss and salvation. I was almost free."

We sit quietly. I think of the deep significance of that which Shanti Devi has told me. Her story about her experiences during the period of death have naturally no value as evidence. It is subjective; there were no witnesses.

What has happened after Shanti Devi's birth on the other hand, has been objectively proven. All her statements have been found to be absolutely correct.

Why shouldn't her recollections from the period in between her reincarnations be as true, believable and genuine?

You may be the judge!

I reincarnated to still my longings

Shanti Devi and I have once again been sitting for hours without a break and spoken to each other. Her humility when confronted with her unusual experiences makes her story even more credible.

There is no land of the dead, I think to myself. No Dante's Inferno, no paradise, no hell. Everything we experience is just a state of consciousness.

This subject is the most delicate, the most subtle and at the same time the most important of all. Nobody can be released from it, nobody can flee from it. It overwhelms us all, happy and unhappy, rich and poor, wise as well as foolish.

What then has Lugdi Devi/Shanti Devi to teach us? Will her example inspire us with hope where words and ceremonies no longer have any meaning?

Will it show us something new or rather arouse an ancient knowledge which has been lost because we have forgotten its significance.

Good people, inspired people, religious people have

repeated their conviction that there is an inner life and a life after death—and they have continually spoken to deaf ears! Yet, why have they continued throughout the ages? Why have they not become silent?

"What everyone wants to achieve is the utmost happiness, the most exalted bliss. You learned one of the methods used to attain an enduring reunion with the Divine, but you weren't successful. You were forced to reincarnate."

"I made a mistake," answers Shanti Devi. "I was far too eager to come back to earth again."

"What power was it that forced you back?"

"It was a longing to see my son and a yearning for Kedar Nath. Perhaps my longing to see my son was the most powerful factor. I was just yearning to come back and was full of love; yet it is quite right to feel love."

"Did you love Kedar Nath more than you loved Krishna?"

"All the memories from my life on Earth returned. I saw Kedar Nath. I saw myself as a bride. I heard his voice. I remembered the yellow house. Everything came back to me as if I had still been on Earth. I wanted to be Kedar Nath's wife again. The memories of my experiences on Earth threw themselves upon me. It was as if in incarnation after incarnation I had met a man who reminded me of Kedar Nath. As if I had incessantly loved Kedar Nath and that he would be pulled away from me. However, I had found him, I seemed to have owned him more and more every time and he did eventually become my husband."

My yearning brought me back

"You mean that the same basic motives, the same basic theme always recurs in our reincarnations? That we always come back to the ones we love? That we cannot flee from those we hate? That happiness as well as unhappiness returns to us?"

"Yes, that is my understanding. We have the same opportunities handed out to us time and time again. Then it depends upon how well we have developed. If we have learned from our experiences and become better human beings. If we have improved then our opportunities also become more abundant."

"If you hadn't known that you were Lugdi Devi, but had just been born and lived a normal life as Shanti Devi, would you perhaps have married a man who reminded you of Kedar Nath, without understanding the secret reason? You would just have found him. Can this perhaps be the explanation as to why we feel drawn to certain individuals and why we feel love at first sight? Neither those who love nor those who hate can be separated by death."

"Hate doesn't really exist," says Shanti Devi. "It's more a question of lack of love, a vacuum which has to be filled. The best way to help others is to love."

"You loved Kedar Nath. You loved your son. Then you must have acted in the right manner?"

"My love was egotistical. It was greedy and demanding. I had a thirst and a hunger for Kedar Nath. I made demands on my son, demands on those nearest and dearest to me. It was desire on a low, egotistical level. The best proof that you truly love someone is that you can allow him or her to be parted from you without feeling bitterness. Otherwise it's only egotism.

"I still loved myself even when I was dead. Therefore

I had to experience death's third stage, reincarnation. If I had concentrated upon Krishna and continued to repeat his name, then my consciousness wouldn't have had any place for desire or anything other than the good, the exalted and the sacred. Then the voice, my own voice from my own subconsciousness would have repeated Krishna's name all the time. But now there were so many other voices from my past lives, voices which I had loved, voices which I demanded to hear again. That was the reason why I didn't hear Krishna's name anymore. Then it happened."

There is life in everything

"What happened? You were drawn into the womb?"

"Yes, exactly as it had happened all the previous times. I have become stronger with each and every incarnation, more independent and a better person. Yet I was still not sufficiently developed. Therefore, I had to come back. Life and the development of consciousness progresses from level to level, from form to form."

"You mean that there is life even in a stone, in earth?"

"Yes, a sort of slumbering, unaware life. Bound energy. It is this sort of energy which is exploited in every possible way: as electricity, as atomic power and so on. A stone isn't aware and therefore it can only effect certain rhythmical changes. A plant begins to have some sort of vague awareness, very vague. An animal has instincts and is a lot more conscious but is unable to understand any connection. A human being knows and can perceive and influence different situations. He or she can think, ask and explain. Yet most human beings still don't know who they really are."

"In the west people speak vaguely about the soul without understanding or admitting that the soul is composed of a number of different organs. They have no names for them. They cannot think about them or understand them and that is most unfortunate. The Indians have preserved this knowledge."

"Westerners feel pursued and chase around in a hurry. They want to earn money, they want to buy happiness and buy love. They want to pay for everything. They don't dare believe that heaven is within them. They dismiss spiritual matters with contempt, indifference or ridicule. It's most unfortunate and regrettable."

I experienced my birth

We sit quietly a while and then Shanti Devi continues to talk about her experiences during the last stage before her birth.

"When I was drawn into the womb the light disappeared. It was as if I had been forced into a narrow dark cell. My sense of time and space came back to me. It was dark and hot, and I was greatly bothered by an unwholesome repugnant smell. It was such a terrible stench that dominated everything."

"So our sense of smell is the first sense to return?"

"Yes, the sense of smell is the last thing to leave a person when he dies and the first to come back when he is born again. It is followed by hearing. It is in that order that the senses have developed in human beings and animals from the beginning of time.

"In the womb I was blind and deaf, as I said, but I had a sense of smell in the beginning. Even this disappeared soon and then I was without sensory impressions. Yet I could feel something which was like pain or happiness. I reacted as my mother did, but I don't remember any details about this.

"Eventually I was pulled out under enormous pain. At the same time I became free. My senses began to expand, I was reincarnated. However, memories of my experiences during the state of death came back to me. I opened my eyes and was absolutely still. I cried quietly to myself without knowing why.

"Then I began to remember Kedar Nath and my home in Muttra and myself as Lugdi Devi. I could not understand that I was not Lugdi Devi who I ought to have been. Eventually I realized that I am both Lugdi Devi and Shanti Devi. That Shanti Devi is Lugdi Devi's next form of development."

Everything is one

Twilight falls. Taj Mahal, the incredibly beautiful marble palace, is bathed in moonlight. A horse-carriage takes us back to the town.

"I have never told anyone else what I have told you now," says Shanti Devi. "You alone have my complete confidence. I know that you understand me."

In Agra we visit Shanti Devi's beautiful sister, Har Pyari, and her husband, Fateh Bahadur. They live in a house which is similar to a bungalow. It's a charming place, perhaps somewhat primitive by western standards, but most pleasant.

In the open courtyard the family's children are playing. The little ones are wildly delighted that so many guests have come to visit. Rang Bahadur is so happy to be able to play with his grandchildren, who he hasn't seen for a long time.

We have arrived in time for dinner. The host goes to

fetch a pitcher of water so that everyone may rinse their hands before the meal.

The sisters carry the appetizing dishes out into the courtyard, where we eat at a beautifully well-laid table.

Night approaches. I'm invited to stay for the night.

Before bedtime, Shanti Devi and I go for a walk across the fields nearby and have the opportunity to talk a little more. She tells me that she, together with some friends, has constituted an organization which has members in Delhi and Calcutta. The purpose is to spread knowledge about reincarnation.

It becomes dark and everyone goes to bed. I am given the best room in the house, with the best bed.

I lie in bed and watch how the rays of the moon caress a picture of Krishna which is standing in a niche in the wall.

I think that all human beings are connected with each other—in life and death. I believe that all human beings, animals, nature, time, space ... everything is part of a whole, that everything is united, that everything belongs together.

Thirty years later

The story about Shanti Devi which you have now read was written more than thirty years ago.

During the time which has passed, Shanti Devi and I have had an intensive correspondence with each other. We have even met again in person in Delhi.

She is extremely well-known

Delhi is warm, hectic, dirty—and beautiful. Amidst the swarm of people it ought to be virtually impossible to find Shanti Devi's home in Chirakhana, an ancient, colorful, odorous and crowded part of Old Delhi.

However, it is not difficult at all. The first person I speak to, a middle-aged well-dressed gentleman, knows where she lives. He asks a younger man to show me the way.

We walk quickly. I am really eager to meet Shanti Devi again.

"She is extremely well-known, everyone knows who she is," says my guide.

Soon we have arrived at Shanti Devi's house, which in

the Indian manner is more open than closed. One can just walk in. It's not even necessary to knock.

I catch sight of Shanti Devi at a distance. She is sitting in an armchair reading a book. I have always thought that she is very beautiful. Her maturity only emphasizes that impression. Yet she looks so youthful.

I have not let her know that I would be coming to see her today. She turns her head, she is not surprised to see me. Her eyes reflect a warm glance of recognition when she discovers me.

"Shanti Devi!"

"Namash te, shri Sture. I knew that you would come."

"Today?"

"Of course, today!"

She greets me with the ancient Indian word "shri" to honor me. We laugh and are happy about being together again.

I am overwhelmed for a moment with the feeling of being in the home of one of the world's most remarkable women, who has attracted such a great deal of attention worldwide.

"My mother, Prem Pyari, is dead. It has caused us great sorrow. She was seriously ill but she received help from Krishna."

"Do you still believe as strongly in Krishna as you used to?"

"Naturally. I see him as a blaze of light."

"Are you interested in Christianity?"

"Yes, and Islam and Parsism as well. I teach Sanskrit which, for Hindus, is both a religion and a philosophy. I teach mostly philosophy, as it's the most important thing for us all.

"I'm only interested in the truth," says Shanti Devi. "The truth which unites all religions and which leads us to God."

Kedar Nath is dead

Rang Bahadur, who is now called Babu, comes into the room. He doesn't work any longer. Now he spends most of his time looking after the house. He recognizes me and welcomes me amiably.

Father and daughter help each other put onto the table newly baked chapati bread and raita alu and other delicacies which smell delicious. We talk about friends we have in common.

"Kedar Nath is dead," says Rang Bahadur.

"How do you feel about Kedar Nath after all these years?" I ask Shanti Devi.

"The relationship between Lugdi Devi and Kedar Nath was perhaps not as romantic as Lugdi Devi supposed it to be. Kedar Nath was rather demanding when it concerned financial matters. Lugdi Devi's father was almost ruined after he collected enough money for the dowry. And I shall never forget those 150 rupees which Kedar Nath had promised me he would offer as a sacrifice to Krishna, but instead paid my funeral with them.

"However, he was absolutely not an unkind person," she continues. "Besides, it was Lugdi Devi's free will to marry him; and he really loved her."

For dessert follows rasgulla, a practically unknown delicacy in the West, which can only be described as a sort of artificial fruit made of milk, honey and lemons.

Rasgulla can effectively quiet the most engaging and exciting conversation.

Shanti Devi teaches

It's evening when Shanti Devi and I make our way out into the town in an open taxicab. It has cooled down somewhat. The air is filled with spicy fragrances.

Old Delhi is like a labyrinth, a chaos of debris from old ruins, old walls partly falling apart, parts of vaulted arches, minarets, paths which one doesn't know where they originally came from or where they lead to.

Everywhere there are swarms of people of all kinds, street vendors, beggars, invalids, elegantly dressed women. A multicolored woven part of karma's cloth.

Shanti Devi talks engagingly about her ashram which is now being built with the help of voluntary workers.

After several days of intensive time spent together we visit the building-site together. We talk a great deal about her vision and about her teaching.

"There is only one God, but he has many names. Everywhere in the Rig Veda and the other Veda books it says explicitly that there is only one God. God is one and the same in Asia and in Europe, in your country as in mine, in my religion as in yours. Hinduism is consequently a monotheistical religion. God appears in different forms only to make it easier for us to understand his many different aspects. The wise perceive him as an abstract force or phenomenon while everyone else wants more concrete evidence. They believe that he is like a person, a prince or a hero and paint pictures of him and portray him with all the characteristics which they believe belong to him. The more primitive the understanding of God is, the less sophisticated the conception is. We consider that the worshipping of Idols is only temporary."

Shanti Devi delivers a short lecture for me. She is an extremely intelligent and mature person but still has something of a child's playfulness about her.

I'm still waiting

The evening when I must leave Delhi has arrived. Shanti Devi and I walk together down by the Jumna, Krishna's holy river.

We talk about her unique experiences and about what significance they have made towards her personal development and growth as a human being.

"Actually, nothing has happened," says Shanti Devi with a smile. "I'm still waiting for that miracle ..."

In every age in every culture, reincarnation has been discussed as a possibility, a hypothesis. Many of history's most brilliant characters have been familiar with the belief in reincarnation. But our chaotic times are not easily satisfied with belief or hypothesis, but demand facts, proof and rational explanations.

After the completed work of the Committee of inquiry, nobody has questioned the authenticity of reincarnation in the case of Shanti Devi. She is living proof that reincarnation is true.

When reincarnation is a proven fact in one case, it must be a reality for everyone else. The laws of life cannot be eluded - - and they are alike for everyone.

For people who have eyes to see and ears to hear, it becomes the inevitable consequence, whether they want it or not, that a whole new worldly concept is brought to light, compared to the understanding of life which only acknowledges one life.

Photo of Shanti Devi by Sture Lönnerstrand.

The case of Shanti Devi

I have endeavored to give as true and living picture as possible of what had happened in "the case of Shanti Devi," as it is usually called. This is the most known and the most well-documented case of reincarnation in the world in modern times.

I have also tried somewhat to characterize the main characters in the drama concerning Shanti Devi.

They are all normal, healthy and intelligent people. But of course, they have a different cultural background than ours in the West.

My investigation is finished, the report is written. It's here that the story about Shanti could end. But I choose, in the following short paragraphs to emphasize the most important links in the chain which definitely prove that Lugdi Devi was reincarnated as Shanti Devi.

1. Shanti Devi's reminiscences were first noticed when she was just four years old. Before that time she had hardly any verbal contact with those around her.

2. From the very beginning, Shanti Devi spoke several dialectic words and expressions which were not understood by her relatives and not even known to them, but which were well-known in and typical for the town of Mathura (Muttra).

   Shanti Devi's relatives had not any opportunity whatsoever to teach her these words. Nor had any people who spoke or knew about this dialect had any contact with Shanti Devi.
3. From the very beginning, Shanti Devi explained that she was a member of a Brahmin family. She alluded to circumstances under which a Brahmin family live and which she said she was used to. Her parents belonged to another group.

   The four-year-old girl could not possibly know about details concerning the Brahmins and their habits.
4. Already from the age of four, Shanti Devi was prepared to travel to Muttra (Mathura). Muttra was the place she felt was her home. It wasn't only to her parents but even to neighbors, for instance the lawyer, Tara Chand Mathur, to whom she had expressed this wish.
5. Influenced as she was by Lugdi Devi's social apprehension, Shanti Devi didn't want to disclose her husband's identity to anyone, not even her parents. It was only when she had been promised that she would be allowed to travel to Muttra and meet her husband in her previous incarnation that she revealed his name.
6. Lugdi Devi's last conscious thoughts were centered upon Krishna, his name and image, according to Shanti Devi's own telling. This is believable when one remembers Lugdi Devi's utterance to her

mother on her deathbed. Shanti Devi's first mem—ory was also associated with an image of Krishna.

7. Not one piece of information that Shanti Devi has given about her circumstances in her previous life has shown to be incorrect.

   The yellow house, for instance, which turned out to be white, had really been yellow during the time when Lugdi Devi lived there. The well in the backyard and the hiding place for the money could not have been fantasized or communicated by anyone else.

8. At the first meeting with her husband from her previous life, Kedar Nath, he declared himself to be his older brother.

   But Shanti Devi wasn't easily fooled. She knew immediately that she stood in front of her husband from her previous incarnation, which shows that she knew him well. She even immediately identified Kedar Nath's cousin, Kanji Mal, when she met him for the first time. She was not quite nine years old then.

9. The child Shanti Devi's behavior towards her husband, Kedar Nath, was that of a decent Indian housewife. Towards her son she showed obvious motherly feelings.

10. Shanti Devi gave her husband from her previous life correct answers about valid circumstances in his and her former private life which none other than Lugdi Devi could possibly know about.

11. Nothing indicates that Shanti Devi had been subjected to any influence or "help" prior to the journey to Muttra.

    In the close-knit Indian family, the children are more dependent on their parents than in the West and their sense of kinship is stronger. The girl Shanti Devi was supervised the whole time by her parents. There is nothing which suggests she may have in some way been hypnotized or influenced.

12. Shanti Devi's parents did nothing whatsoever to encourage her reminscences from her previous life in Muttra. On the contrary, they tried to persuade her to forget these memories, in accordance with the Indian conception that a child can suffer severely, even die, if it remembers its previous life and comes into contact with people who were closely related with it in its previous life.
13. Her parents did not take any initiative to investigate the amount of truth alleged in their daughter's story. On the contrary, they were totally against it, for as long as possible.

    They gave their consent only after strong pressure, from none other than Mahatma Gandhi himself.
14. The Committee of inquiry was conducted by three of Delhi's most highly-respected citizens: Lala Deshbandu Gupta, the chairman of the Indian Publisher's Association, who was also an M.P., Neki Ram Sharma, M.P. and Tara Chand Mathur, one of Delhi's most prominent lawyers.

    It's hard to believe that these people would have committed themselves in an undertaking which had the slightest tinge of falsity. Their participation in the committee of inquiry was a guarantee that the investigation was performed impartially and from all points of view in a satisfactory manner. All three had experience in "investigations," each with their own special point of view.
15. Every minute during the visit to Muttra, Shanti

Devi was under careful supervision which prevented her from taking instructions from anyone.

16. When the girl met her mother from her previous life, she called attention to circumstances which did not concern anyone other than the mother and her daughter Lugdi Devi—circumstances which Shanti Devi could not possibly have known other than by remembering her previous life.
17. During the journey to Muttra, as well as on earlier occasions, all her reactions, as far as one could tell were characterized by sincerity.

    The child Shanti Devi's behavior in certain situations was what one normally would expect from the grown-woman Lugdi Devi. This reinforces the impression of authenticity.
18. A proven case of reincarnation is such a powerful occurrence even in India that it could very easily have been taken advantage of financially and in various ways exploited by her parents if they had wished to do so. But nothing indicates that they have made the slightest attempt in that direction.

    The case of Shanti Devi can therefore not be the result of a smart conspiracy where the purpose was aimed at making a profit, or used to advantage in some way.
19. The idea of reincarnation is one of the most important fundamentals in Indian religion and cannot be taken lightly.

    It is consequently out of the question that any of the people involved in the drama concerning Shanti Devi should have condescended to participate in any kind of deception.
20. Shanti Devi herself is an extremely intelligent and cultivated person, whether regarded from an Indian

or western point of view.

Taking into consideration her religious, ethical and moral background, it is absolutely impossible to imagine that she would participate in any form of deception.

21. Due to her own personal experience, reincarnation is to this day an obvious reality for Shanti Devi.

    Throughout her whole life she has abstained from personal financial gain in spreading the message about her experiences. She considers it to be her natural duty, her true calling in life to inform people of the law of karma and reincarnation, and to do so free of charge.

22. Shanti Devi has always felt herself morally tied by "her" marriage to Kedar Nath Chaubey, even though this was part of her life as Lugdi Devi.

    According to the Indian conception, a woman's duty is to be married and bear children and people have often reminded her about this. But she has not been able to remarry, as she still regards herself as being married to Kedar Nath.

This gives an outline of the tremendous urgency and powerful active influences in Shanti Devi's reminiscences and the crucial effect they have had upon her life.

2

Reincarnation and Karma

A person's personal history doesn't begin with the body with which he first saw the light of day. Neither does it end with the body in which he will die.

The truth is that we will live again and die again until that time comes when we have fulfilled our supreme destiny which brought us down to Earth.

As long as a human being has not achieved this purpose, for example, to be permanently united with the Divine, then he cannot avoid being reincarnated. This is applicable whether he likes it or not, whether he loves this world or hates it.

That most of us do not remember our previous lives is not a valid argument against reincarnation.

Sometimes we have difficulty remembering what we did a week ago, not to mention what happened a year ago, or ten years ago.

Yet, there is nobody who would even think that this very normal state of forgetfulness should prove that we were not present on these occasions in the past.

Nor can anyone with proven credibility state that just because we have forgotten our earlier incarnations, it proves that we never existed then.

It is far more sensible to contemplate the reason for this merciful forgetfulness.

The answer is naturally that we shall devote ourselves to the present incarnation with all our energy and concentration, without letting ourselves be disturbed by regrettable memories from the past.

Shanti Devi maintains that we must incarnate innumerable times before we are able to profit from all the necessary experiences we have gained, and finally be able to enter into a lasting union with God.

We move from one body to another, from one reincarnation to the next, and we are developing the whole time.

An important question is, of course, what sort of power it is which makes it possible for us to be constantly reborn in new bodies?

Shanti Devi gives two answers to this question, based upon her own experiences which took place during her death.

Her intense longing for her son and her husband, her general longing to live, drove her inexorably towards a speedy reincarnation—in spite of the fact that she wanted to be reunited with Brahma, the Godhead. However, her yearning to come back to Earth was stronger. It gained control over her.

She also tells that during her death experience she felt a strong wish to improve, to attain a greater personal perfection. This inherent will towards constant development also contributed to her being led back into the reincarnation process.

The law of karma

Thereby her latent karmic heritage began to be activated and take form in her coming incarnation: biological factors, such as body, in what family she would be born, her surroundings, *etc.* plus psychological factors such as temperament, attitude, habits, and spiritual life.

Everyone I spoke to in Muttra made it quite clear that Lugdi Devi had been an almost saint-like being through her unselfishness and religious convictions.

Where should such a person be reborn if not into a family which was characterized by a similar spiritual atmosphere? Her mother, Prem Pyari, was a warmly religious person. Her father, Rang Bahadur, was also religious, although to a somewhat lesser degree.

In this home there was an understanding and an encouragement for the little Shanti Devi's heart-felt longing for God. In this environment she could once again pick up the threads from Lugdi Devi's time without any difficulty and further develop the religious interests which had been so pronounced in her earlier incarnation. As a grown woman, Shanti Devi has matured into a competent and gentle instructor and teacher for those endeavoring to seek perfection.

This is a clear and practical example of how the law of karma operates from life to life.

Karma is the universal principle which is constantly striving to replace lost balance and lack of harmony.

In the Christian religion sowing and harvesting is talked about—a very well-founded and true description.

Sowing in this case means that we inherit ourselves, that we become "our own children." It's only our physical body which is inherited from our parents.

The significance of the law of karma is that we may

reap the benefits of our thoughts, feeling, attitudes, words and deeds in our present or in some future incarnation.

It is important to understand that the law of sowing and reaping is always in our favor. It offers us constantly new possibilities to grow in experience, insight and maturity.

It is a mistake to believe that karma is only about retribution and punishment for committed sins. The opposite is also true, that is, that we may enjoy the consequences of uplifted thoughts and unselfish behavior.

Shanti Devi talks about how the law of karma makes it possible for us to have experiences which help us to overcome old weaknesses and develop new talents as well.

Factors creating karma are firstly thoughts, feelings and desires, but also words and actions.

The thoughts are of course the most important because deeds are created by thoughts. Words and deeds are materialized thoughts.

The whole of our past lives are within us. Every event in our present life is the result of a number of causal connections from both our present and our earlier incarnations.

Those who have the courage to think this through to the end will realize that past incarnations influence our lives more profoundly than we can imagine at first.

Shanti Devi emphazizes that a knowledge of the law of karma guides us towards a genuine love for every living being.

"The thoughts you have today will characterize your destiny for always," she says.

The creative forces of reincarnation

Shanti Devi's experiences give us an extremely valuable insight into those forces which create and control our lives—what they are, and how they appear from one incarnation to the next. There is therefore, good reason to elaborate further upon this.

The desire to live. The initial primordial force which inexorably leads us back to new earthly lives, is our longing for life; our thirst for life.

It's a question of an indomitable need of taking on a physical form so that consiousness can develop itself and fulfill itself, along with its inherent possibilities on the physical plane. As long as this primary thirst for life has not been quenched (by an everlasting union with the Godhead), we will reincarnate in new bodies.

Like Shanti Devi, we yearn incessantly until that moment when we are once again able to put on our earthly costume and continue where we left off in our previous incarnation.

The desire for personal and spiritual development. Besides the primary thirst for life, Shanti Devi could discern a closely related, but clearly different impulse, a wish to continue her personal and spiritual development. This desire contributed to driving her towards the new incarnation.

Here it's a question of the ego's desire to constantly improve, to continuously develop new skills and talents, to take further steps towards perfection. This desire to develop is a driving force. The aim is that the ego will attain higher and higher levels on the spiral-formed ladder of development. This development has two sides to it, partly the ego's striving to acquire a greater degree of proficiency and knowledge about itself, about it's own psychology (personal development). Partly an intensified yearning to be able to live in harmony with the Godhead (spiritual development).

Karma. The third powerful force which is conducive to forming our body and environment, is our personal, karmic heritage. The whole of our past lives are within us.

The past forms the present. Our life today is the fruit of yesterday's thoughts and actions. Our future life will be formed by our present thoughts, feelings, words and actions.

By analyzing your present thoughts and actions, you will have a good idea as to how your next incarnation will be formed. The individual who clearly understands the incredible, creative power of thought, does not dare to entertain negative thoughts!

These are the three main forces which lead to reincarnation and which determine how the new incarnation will develop. Our thirst for life which drives us towards a new reincarnation, a new life on Earth. Our inherent desire to continue developing, which urges us to continually strive towards attaining higher goals: and lastly, our karmic heritage, which specifies the conditions and prerequisites in our life to come.

Reincarnation: a historical perspective

In the past the teaching of reincarnation was generally widespread everywhere in Asia, Africa, America and Europe. It was even the religion of the primeval tribes of Australia.

Five hundred years before the birth of Christ, the Greek poet Pindar wrote, for example, that the soul is gradually purified through the process of being reincarnated into different newly created bodies.

Pythagoras explained it like this:

"After death, the soul enters into the land of the bodyless where it must free itself from all its faults. Then it must once again inhabit a body and commence a new earthly life. This will be created in a way which corresponds with the soul's moral nature."

In Plato's *Phaedo*, Socrates is quoted as saying:

"Man has since ancient times thought it quite possible that the soul, after having left this world, descends to the underworld where it departs by degrees and returns to life. In this way the soul wanders from death to birth, from life to new life ... Time and time again the soul is called back to earth."

Plotinus, the major representative of Neoplatonism said:

"The soul goes through different forms of existence. Our present existence was created as a result of our actions in the past."

Josephus, a Jewish historian, described the Essenes as believing in reincarnation:

"They are of the opinion that their bodies are destroyed, as the matter the bodies are made of is not permanent, but that their souls continue, saved from death by God's mercy."

The Essenes are thought to be an orientally-influenced order of Jewish monks. They were pre-Christian but they had certain kinds of beliefs and rules of discipline which were similar to what later was practiced in Christian monasteries.

Ovid, a Roman poet, wrote that the secret of the grave is also the secret of the cradle:

"Why fear death? Souls are not suppressed by the power of death. When they are set free from the mortal cover they wear today, they will soon return in a new bodily form."

The fathers of the church

The Christian church fathers generally had their roots in the Greek cultural sphere and believed in reincarnation. This religious belief was applicable moreover, according to St. Hieronymus, "to the greater part of the West."

Origen, who lived and worked in the 3rd century is considered to have been one of the most important fathers of the church. He was strongly influenced by Plato, who in the dialog *Phaedo* even described the soul's longing for rebirth as a longing for love.

Compare Shanti Devi's recollection from her death experience, that it was her longing for her son and her husband which drove her back to life on Earth.

Pope Anastasius I wrote about the belief in Reincarnation in a letter to Ruffinus that "this concept was general among the older fathers."

Justin the Martyr remarked that "he who has reincarnated is unable to remember his earlier existence."

Reincarnation was taken seriously by all the gnostic sects and they were for a time more numerous than any other Christian group.

The majority of the first Christians believed in the teachings of reincarnation.

Jews, Romans and Celts

The theory of reincarnation is intimately connected with the Jewish mystical philosophy.

In the book *Zohar*, which is about mystical Judaism, it says (II, 142:46) "that those who have not accomplished their destiny are sent back to life to complete it."

In *Zohar* it is also described how biblical individuals return to life on Earth to settle up their affairs, for example, Abel and Benjamin.

The Romans had perhaps been informed about the secret of reincarnation. Perhaps from the Greeks, or even the Etruscans from whom they had gotten so many other things.

They may have been given a more philosophical version of Pythagoras, who according to a persistent rumor acquired his knowledge of reincarnation in India.

Caesar wrote the following in his book about the Gallic war:

"The (Druids) want to impress upon us that it is one of their fundamental principles that the soul is not destroyed but only leaves one body to go to another. This results in their being driven to develop themselves without having any fear of death."

When Diodorus, a Greek historian, wrote about the Celts, he emphasized that the teachings of Pythagoras were predominant among them. "Their souls are thought to be immortal. All that can happen to them at the most, is that they may have to live for a number of years in another body.

"Perhaps this is the key to the well-known Celtic bravery."

Quotations from the Bible

Several Bible quotations indicate that the belief in reincarnation, at the time when Jesus appeared on Earth, was generally accepted among the Jews. Here are several quotations:

Jesus asked his disciples: "Who do men say that I, the Son of man, am?" (Matthew 16:13)

The disciples answered: "Some say that you are John the Baptist: some, Elias; and others, Jeremias, or one of the prophets."

If it was not for the fact that reincarnation was generally accepted within the Jewish culture, Jesus would hardly have asked the question in that manner.

Observe that Jesus asked who the people believed he was, not if he had lived before. He took for granted that everyone knew about prior lifetimes.

Another famous remark (John 15:27) which is ascribed to Jesus, is as follows:

"And you also shall bear witness, because you have been with me from the beginning."

The beginning must have alluded to the first words in the Bible, "In the beginning ..." It was a question of a rather long period of time.

In another passage (John 9:2), the disciples asked Jesus: "Master, who did sin, this man or his parents, that he was born blind?"

The question implies, that for the disciples it was quite natural that the man had been inflicted with a handicap due to the fact that he had sinned in a earlier life. It could not have happened in the present incarnation, as he had been blind since birth.

St. Clement of Alexandria stated that the teachings of reincarnation had been authorized by the apostle Paul himself. In a letter to the Galatians (Galatians 6:7) Paul says:

"Be not deceived; God is not mocked: for whatsoever a man soweth, that shall he also reap."

Paul knew that everything a person sows during an earthly life cannot possibly be reaped during the same lifetime. Sometimes God's mills grind slowly.

Paul's successors have not, as far as is known, ever questioned the Law regarding sowing and reaping, or the Law of consequences, as it is also called.

However, to this day, one has apparently overlooked the fact that Karma and Reincarnation are two sides of the same coin. Reincarnation is not possible without karma and karma cannot function without reincarnation.

There are other places in the New Testament as well as in the Old Testament that suggest reincarnation, but they are less well known.

Elijah and John the Baptist

The Bible's prime example, regarding the truth of reincarnation is clearly shown by Jesus himself. The Old Testament and the New Testament come together in an extremely interesting manner where the prophet Elijah, who according to the account in the Old Testament (II Kings 2:11), "… went up to heaven in a chariot of fire."

The Old Testament concludes with the following prophecy: "Lo, I will send you the prophet Elijah …" (Malachi 4:5).

The New Testament attaches great importance to the question regarding the rebirth of Elijah and has consequently, taken up the subject in several places:

In Luke (1:17) "Elijah's spirit and power" is talked about, which in the body of John the Baptist would come before the Lord.

In the Gospel according to Mark (Mark 9:11) the disciples ask: "Why do the scribes say that Elijah must come first?" Jesus answers them, that Elijah would indeed come first to restore all things (Mark 9:12).

In Matthew (17:12) Jesus is quoted as saying: "But I tell you that Elijah has already come … ." "Then the disciples understood that it was John The Baptist he was speaking to them about" (Matthew 17:13).

In Matthew (11:14–15) Jesus is as clear as crystal about John the Baptist's earlier identity. "And if you are willing to accept it, **he is ELIJAH**, the one who is to come." He then adds, so there can be no doubt about it: "Whoever has ears ought to hear."

Can it be said more clearly?

Jesus has with these words, once and for all established the truth of reincarnation.

"Whoever has ears ought to hear!"

The teachings of reincarnation, although still rejected,

are nonetheless an important part of the Christian heritage, a cornerstone in the original conception of Christianity, and a basis for the original picture of Christianity throughout the world—in a similar manner that the belief in reincarnation has always been in the oriental religions.

It's important to ascertain that the belief in repeated earthly lives is in no way in conflict with central Christian motives. It's more likely that the teaching of reincarnation strengthens the Christian message, making it more complete, more genuine and more credible.

Many people have wondered how it is possible that Jesus, Christianity's central figure, can still be denied and be so flagrantly misunderstood by his own followers, by his own churches, regarding such an important and fundamental question concerning what happens to us when we die.

It's an enigma which remains unsolved.

The monks of the middle ages

Despite the ancient belief in reincarnation all over the world, the monks of the medieval times [600–1400 A.D.] succeeded in the feat of banning the teachings of reincarnation.

But it is even more remarkable that this dogma still exists after almost 1,500 years, and that it is taken seriously by people in our enlightened age.

It was not possible to abandon in a single blow the inherited, deeply rooted insight about the truth of rebirth. It happened in stages and was finally forbidden through the official condemnation of the church father Origen by the ecumenical council in Constantinople in the 6th century.

There has been much speculation as to why it was so important for the church to drive through a decision which was not only in conflict with its own roots, against the better judgement of its own church fathers, but also against a many thousand-year-old traditional belief from all parts of the World.

In the middle of the 6th century the church had managed to become a powerful factor in the powerful eastern Roman Empire which was governed by the Emperor Justinian.

A hypothesis which has been brought forward, is that it made it easier for the church to practice their power and dominate people. Should people not do what the priest said, they were threatened with eternal suffering and damnation after this only life which the church had made a decision about. And to tempt them with the delights of Paradise for all who followed the priestly instructions without making a fuss, rather than allow the people to accept full responsibility for their lives and deeds.

However, this is naturally just speculation. We shall never know what political reasons and considerations, including those by the Emperor himself, led to this decision. A decision which had such incalculable consequenses for the countries in the West and thereby for the whole world.

Regardless of what the motives might have been, they are now in the past. Christianity is now free to return to the church fathers' belief.

The Pope has the power to change

As a result of the way it has handled the question of reincarnation, the church has accrued a karmic debt towards mankind.

This occurred due to the fact that it first ignored, or rather, defied Jesus Christ's explicit teachings about the ancient knowledge of reincarnation which are mentioned in the Bible.

This ancient knowledge was believed by people everywhere on Earth. The church then continued to mislead the people about this fundamental existential question for 15 centuries.

These are strong words—but true.

What then, can the church do, to begin to pay off its karmic debt?

The Pope has power, like no other human being, to influence and change the thoughts of millions of people. If he admits that the church's understanding about the question of reincarnation is incorrect, great things will begin to take place.

Besides, he can, if he wishes, ask mankind for forgiveness for all the suffering that has been caused during all those years, both for single individuals and for mankind as a whole, due to the church's decision which was made in the Middle Ages.

This is, without a doubt, the most important step the church can take in our present age to contribute towards improving the spiritual state of mankind. Such an initiative would also make it easier for other religious organizations to venture to take an equivalent step.

The attitude towards the question of reincarnation, more and more poses a serious threat towards the church's credibility and future. A change will therefore in all probability, be brought about.

The truth about reincarnation

We discuss today's different questions seriously and with engagement. Our restless thoughts and emotions get caught up on many things, topics great and small. However, there is one subject we don't dare touch upon: what happens to us when we die?

Why is it that most of us repress this fundamental existential question? Why don't we dare to discuss it as openly as we discuss politics and sports, violence and sex?

The usual excuse is, that it is useless to speculate upon the question as we are ignorant in such matters, and that nobody knows anything about death and what happens to us afterwards.

Since all humans die, it's nothing one need worry about. What must happen, happens. Morbid thoughts about death only destroy that happiness which life, in spite of all the disappointments it holds, has to offer us. The question about death is altogether too serious. It demands far too much personal responsibility for us to be able to cope with it.

That's the way it carries on. Decade after decade we repress—in one way or another—the question concerning death and what happens to us afterwards.

However, eventually the problem inexorably catches up with us. It's when death approaches. Then it can no longer be swept under the carpet. For the first time in our life, it's given top priority.

Three alternatives

Throughout the ages, thinkers have grappled with the existential questions. Many of the most outstanding have been convinced of the truth in reincarnation. Others have thought it to be a possibility.

Now, just as before, there are principally three alternatives to choose from:

1. Body and soul are an inseparable unity. When the body dies consciousness is also obliterated. There is no survival in any form. Just total annihilation. The life we are now living is the only life there is, and the only one we'll ever have.
2. What happens to you from the minute you die and up to the last day of judgment, we don't know. Nor do we know when the day of judgment occurs. Perhaps in several million years time? Then the body, which has crumbled to dust or ashes, and the soul reunite, arise again and are judged. The judgment will either be a sentence of everlasting suffering in hell or eternal bliss in Paradise, according to how you have managed to conduct the only, remote earthly life you were granted.

3. Consciousness leaves the body after the body has ceased to function. After some time, without having had contact with any physical body, your mind (which is the real you) reincarnates in a new, fresh body. Yet another earthly life is begun, whereby you are given the possiblitiy of creating new experiences. The law which says sow and you will reap (karma), always makes sure that you are given a new chance to repair earlier acts of neglect and mistakes you have made.

Which of these conceptions can you live with—and die with? Which divine judicial system is the most believable, and most compatible with the attitude of an all merciful God?

Systems of justice, created by human beings, are mostly in harmony with the third point of view. The criminal who has served his term of punishment, is released. He is given a new chance.

Alternatives two and three have in common that some sort of continuation is taken for granted, that death is not the end—and that even for this reason, there is cause for us to respect laws and rules, and to respect the integrity of other human beings and their rights.

After reading about Shanti Devi and her well-documented life experiences, it must be extremely difficult to uphold the credibility of alternatives one and two. Those who judge discriminatively will reject them both as unreasonable and unworthy.

Personal responsibility

What can then be the consequences for the individual, and for the whole of our civilization, the day the teachings of reincarnation are generally accepted even in the West? When eventually even western priests, churches and religious societies, have allowed themselves to be converted and convinced about the truth of reincarnation, and no longer oppose it.

The conditions for life on our planet are being poisoned, plundered and destroyed at a tremendous speed for the sake of short term gains. This will, without a doubt, present disastrous consequences in the future if drastic measures are not taken to change our way of thinking and acting.

The short term thinking which alternatives one and two awaken and support, accelerate without a doubt the destruction of our environment and the Earth upon which we live.

What could possibly be more important for every human being today, in the vulnerable situation which humanity finds itself, than to try and understand the meaning of life and death? To eagerly study how life and death are connected, how birth and death (like falling asleep at night and waking up in the morning) are changes in a continuous cycle, where one form of life follows the next, just as surely as sleep follows after being awake.

Alternative three (reincarnation) is conducive to the development of a long-term personal acceptance of responsibility, a vision of a future which reaches beyond the present life—and which is not only a responsibility for our own personal future, but for our planet and the whole universe.

The natural attitude would be that we, in our own

interest, as well as the interests of the whole, wholeheartedly try to understand and prepare for the transition which awaits us, and the body-free form of life which follows thereafter.

Shanti Devi has, by her very existence and first-hand reincarnation experiences, given us the best possible inspiration and help in this matter.

Fear of death

Every human being knows by repeated experience, that day is followed by night and that night is followed by day.

We go to bed at night to sleep, without any hesitation, in spite of our consciousness being extinguished, in spite of the fact that the world no longer exists for us even as an idea in our consciousness. How can it be that we feel so utterly confident?

The answer is, of course, that the experience is constantly repeated, that there is always another morning. That creates confidence and security.

What would happen if we had the same insight and conviction about the greater cycle of life and death?

Would the thought of death then lose its sting and its paralyzing fear? Would we then enter the state of death as calmly and confidently as we do in the evening, when we enter into the deep, dreamless sleep?

Lugdi Devi entered into the state of death with this assurance and openness. She had no doubts whatsoever about the fact that she would soon be reincarnated. Death was therefore easier for her to endure than it would otherwise have been.

Suicide

For people who have for some reason found themselves in a state of deepest despair and agony, suicide can seem to be the only solution, the only practicable way to be rid of their troubles.

What happens to such an individual?

Suicide deprives him of his body, but not of his identity and consciousness, nor of his memories, thoughts and feelings. In his bodyless state, he will again and again, without ceasing, relive those thoughts and feelings which preceded and triggered the tragic event.

The body, his instrument, which could have helped him make up for his shortcomings, has been taken away from him. This makes his torment all the worse and all the more difficult to endure—many times over. This, if anything, is hell's inferno.

The person who committed suicide is, in a subsequent incarnation, confronted with a similar situation to that which triggered the suicide. It may cost him many incarnations before he manages to get himself out of the devastating, negative stream of thoughts which at one time, perhaps a very long time ago, led up to the first suicide.

The insight about the truth of reincarnation has prevented many suicides—and thereby, the unbearable anguish and pain which persons who commit suicide, as well as their nearest and dearest, are always subjected to.

Shanti Devi's unique evidence

Shanti Devi has devoted her life to philosophic studies and teaching.

With her own first-hand experience of reincarnation as a background, she reveals in a convincing manner, what positive effects the belief in reincarnation can result in.

We'll be doing ourselves and everyone else a favor if we closely scrutinize and study Shanti Devi's life experiences, in an unprejudiced frame of mind, and consider their significance.

Don't let us miss this opportunity!

Many people have maintained that they remember previous lives. These recollections are certainly of value as evidence, but only for themselves.

It is different with Shanti Devi. In her case, the committee of enquiry carried out its investigation while she was still so young that the family members and other persons from her previous life, whom she had spoken about and made references to, could be reached and interviewed, and her statements thus be verified.

The value of the evidence in the case of Shanti Devi is therefore unique. It is so powerful and convincing that it cannot be ignored by any individual who sincerely seeks the truth.

Our real home

The conception of time has another significance for the individual who is convinced of the truth of reincarnation. He does not feel that he is limited to clock-time as other people are. His conception of time is expanding in a liberating manner.

He knows, like Shanti Devi, that his true identity is a timeless and formless mind which wanders from body to body, and whose real home is beyond time and space, in the eternal now.

Every reincarnation on Earth is regarded by him as a necessary step in the on-going development of his ego-consciousness.

This shift in his conception of time has a healing effect upon his life and consciousness. He has taken a step further and nearer towards his real self.

And lastly …

This book about my Indian friend Shanti Devi Mathur is not only a story about an unusually exciting human destiny and an exceptional human being.

The book also has another purpose, namely, to stimulate the reader to reflect, to contribute to an increased awareness and knowledge about the law of karma, and the signification of the teachings of reincarnation: what they mean and what the conseqences are.

"The more we learn about karma and reincarnation, the better the chances are that we are able to live our lives so that we won't regret afterwards what we did," says Shanti Devi.

Discuss Shanti Devi's experiences. Compare her story with other cases of reincarnation you've heard about.

Be especially aware of what children have to say. They have returned to the physical dimension just a short while ago, and may still have distinct recollections from their previous incarnation. These stories may be of great importance.

Perhaps you yourself have memories from previous lives?

Don't be afraid to recount them. Your experiences may help others to see their lives in a new light, to have a truer understanding about life and its meaning.

The same rules of life for all

Shanti Devi's extremely well documented reincarnation experience is invaluable as a guide for all those seeking the truth. It shows that birth is not the beginning and that death is not the end.

Now that reincarnation has shown itself to be real and proven for one individual, Shanti Devi, then it must also be true for everyone else.

The same rules of life apply to all.

Sture Lönnerstrand was born in Sweden on March 13, 1919. Part of his education was at the University of Lund where he studied medicine, psychology, art history, Nordic languages, Greek, Hebrew and especially Sanscrit. He began his career as a journalist while still at the University, and has been a freelance journalist, author and artist, most of his life. He published his first collection of poetry in 1939, followed by several more collections, plays and novels. He was granted the Bonnier Publishers' novel award in 1954.

He has traveled extensively in different parts of the world both as an author and journalist. He is very familiar with Indian culture, religion and yoga. Also he has an extensive knowledge of Sanscrit which has helped him immensely in his Indian studies.

At the end of the 1950's he wrote a series of articles about SHANTI DEVI which were published in 9 languages. He was the first person in the western world to take an interest in the case of SHANTI DEVI. Her story is now included in many compilations of famous cases of reincarnation.

A statement by Shanti Devi:

With this statement I certify that the Swedish author, Mr. Sture Lönnerstrand, Stockholm, has my full personal confidence regarding my case of reincarnation. He alone has the actual intimate information.

Mr. Lönnerstrand is my only agent and representative in connection with distribution of my life story from all points of view in whatever form it will be, now and for the future.

Any other person who tries to distribute, tell or sell information about me and my case without his permission is doing it without my authority.

Delhi, September 30, 1957. (Signed) Shanti Devi Mathur